Community Health:

issues in management

Eileen O'Keefe

Roger Ottewill

Ann Wall

Business Education Publishers Limited

ISBN 0 907679 42 0

First published in 1992
Reprinted 1994

Published in Great Britain by Business Education Publishers Limited
Leighton House 10 Grange Crescent Stockton Road
Sunderland Tyne and Wear SR2 7BN

Tel. 091 567 4963 Fax. 091 514 3277

British Cataloguing-in-Publications Data
A catalogue record for this book is available from the British Library

Printed in Great Britain by Athenaeum Press Limited
Dukesway Team Valley Gateshead Tyne and Wear

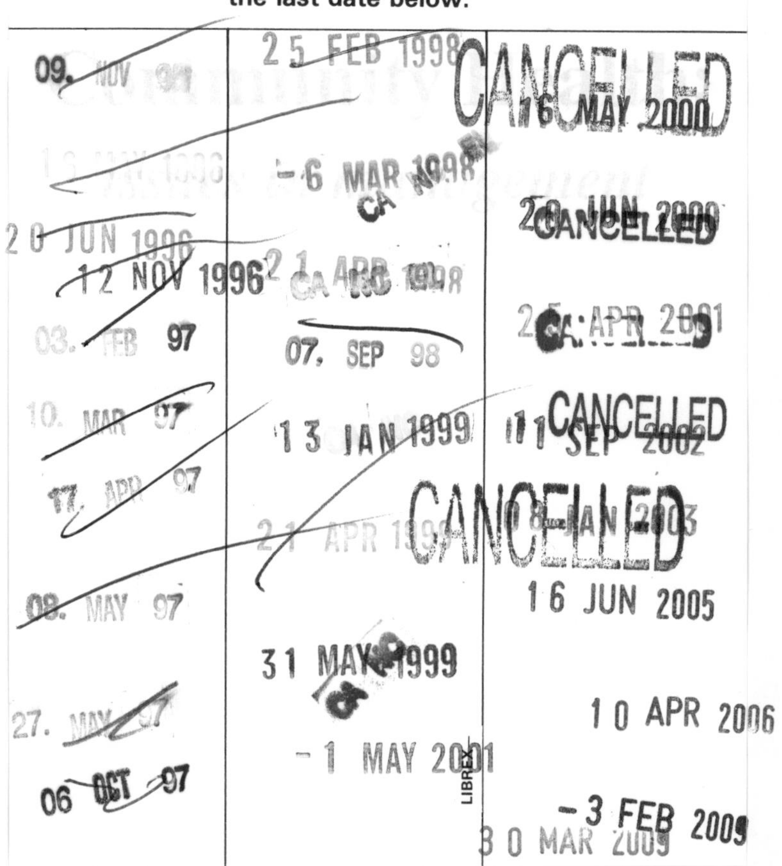
Books are to be returned on or before
the last date below.
LIBREX

P R E F A C E

This book is a companion volume to *The Growth and Development of the Community Health Services* by Roger Ottewill and Ann Wall, published by Business Education Publishers. It is intended, however, to be free standing and to be comprehensible to those who have not read the earlier book.

Many of the issues which we consider here have always been on the agenda of those reponsible for the development and delivery of community based health care services. Nevertheless, in recent years they have been thrown into sharper relief, not only by political initiatives in the sphere of health care such as those related to the three White Papers *Promoting Better Health, Working for Patients and Caring for People*, but also by what has been termed the 'crisis in health'. Moreover we would argue that, in the long run, the 'crisis in health' is likely to have a more profound effect on the management, delivery and status of services than the actions of party politicians. For example, the issues and problems arising from a rapidly ageing population are going to remain on the health care agenda whatever administrative and financial arrangements are in operation.

Thus, in this book the 'crisis in health' serves as a backdrop for our examination of a range of issues, the selection of which has been influenced both by comment on the previous book and our experiences as teachers. It is increasingly the case that students on many different health related courses have, or will have, management responsibilities and are seeking ways of dealing with the problems and challenges which these generate. Thus, from our different academic backgrounds, we have been guided by what we believe to be of particular relevance for the education of those engaged in the management of community health.

The development of the management function, which, in the case of health care, is particularly associated with the recommendations of the Griffiths NHS Management Report, has significantly changed the role of many front line service providers. It has also meant that they have had to take on board perspectives for which their clinical education has not prepared them and work with those from very different backgrounds from their own. In the future this is likely to include service users and informal carers, as well as other professionals. Clearly, this has major implications for the manner in which practising and aspiring managers are educated and trained. In particular, it implies that far greater attention should be given to the development of multidisciplinary approaches to curriculum design, modes of delivery and forms of assessment.

In this book our aim is to contribute to the process through the selection and treatment of issues and the provision of full notes to enable students to use them as a basis for project work and problem based assignments. It is also hoped that by exploring issues in this way we shall make a useful contribution to the wider debate surrounding the future of community based health care services and help to ensure that community provision secures, what we would regard as, its rightful position at the centre, as opposed to the periphery, of the health care system.

In producing this book we have incurred a number of debts. Our thanks go to Christine Hogg, health policy analyst and researcher; to Bernard Jones, John Kingdom and Malcolm Stevens of Sheffield Business School; to Jeannette Murphy of St Bartholomew's Hospital Medical School; to Sue Pike and Jo Skinner of the School of Health Studies, University of North London; to Kathryn Rounce of the North London Joint College of Health Studies; and to Lynda Saunders of Christchurch College, Canterbury, all of whom read and made helpful and constructive comments on early drafts of specific chapters. In addition, we are particularly indebted, and extremely grateful, to Bob Hudson, who read the complete manuscript and provided us with a great deal of encouragement and much food for thought. His comments generated a considerable amount of discussion amongst the three of us and many have been taken on board in preparing the final draft. At the same time, we feel that he has sown the seeds of another book. Of course, for the final version of this book, we accept full responsibility.

We should also like to place on record our thanks to everyone at Business Education Publishers for their contribution to the book's production.

Last, but by no means least, we apologise to our colleagues for our repeated refusal to answer the telephone and to our families for our continuing preoccupation with community health.

Eileen O'Keefe University of North London
Roger Ottewill Sheffield Business School
Ann Wall Sheffield Business School

Figures

Abbreviations

BMA	British Medical Association
CHSs	Community Health Services
DH	Department of Health
DHSS	Department of Health and Social Security
DHA	District Health Authority
DMU	Directly Managed Unit
DPH	Director of Public Health
EOC	Equal Opportunities Commission
FHSs	Family Health Services
FHSA	Family Health Services Authority
FPC	Family Practitioner Committee
GNP	Gross National Product
HFA	Health for All
HVA	Health Visitors' Association
HSs	Hospital Services
IT	Information Technology
MOH	Medical Officer of Health
NHS	National Health Service
OPCS	Office of Population Censuses and Surveys
RAWP	Resource Allocation Working Party
RHA	Regional Health Authority
WHO	World Health Organisation
WHM	Women's Health Movement

Contents

CHAPTER 1

Introduction

The closing years of the twentieth century may be regarded as the worst of times and the best of times for the community health services (CHSs). Stressed communities with rapidly changing health needs present overstretched managers and service providers with ever increasing and often conflicting demands. Moreover, many of the more alert observers suspect that even if additional monies were available this alone would not guarantee the adequate provision of health care in the community. At the same time, they recognise that only a shift towards a more community based approach to health care offers a credible way through the difficulties facing the health and social care system as a whole.

In the opening chapter of *The Growth and Development of the Community Health Services* (Ottewill and Wall), the CHSs were described as:

> *That diverse group of personal health services provided in the community which have a strong proactive orientation in the identification and meeting of need with respect, in particular, to: the promotion of health; the prevention of ill health and the care of vulnerable groups.*[1]

This working definition was derived from an analysis of the functions and objectives of those responsible for managing and delivering the CHSs.

The particular expertise of CHSs staff lies in the following areas: health maintenance and health promotion; disease prevention (including monitoring and referral); rehabilitation and after-care; and pastoral care and counselling. They also contribute, in some contexts, to the diagnosis and treatment of various disorders.[2] In performing these functions service managers and providers should be seeking to make services accessible and acceptable to clients; to identify and meet needs in a systematic manner; to secure 'value for money'; and to adapt to changing circumstances.[3] In so doing, they should be endeavouring to apply the public service values on which the National Health Service (NHS) is founded.

Whereas the CHSs are a distinctive group of services with shared functions and objectives, they are also part of the wider system of health and social care. This includes:

- the other publically provided personal health care services, that is family health services (FHSs) and hospital services (HSs);
- social care services; and
- environmental, occupational and public health services.

In addition, there are those provided by voluntary and private sector agencies.[4] Moreover, all the formally provided services rest on the bedrock of informal care. Not surprisingly, those working in all these areas, whether as formal providers or informal carers, have overlapping interests and concerns. This point is illustrated by Figure 1.1.

The Place of the Community Health Services within the Wider Health and Social Care System

1) ***Examples***
- needs of priority groups (i.e. older people, those with physical disabilities, learning disabilities or mental health problems)
- paramedical services (e.g. occupational therapy)

8) ***Examples***
- epidemiological analysis
- no-smoking policies
- accident prevention

2) ***Examples***
- support for informal carers
- research
- self-help groups
- campaigning

7) ***Examples***
- private nursing homes
- chiropody services
- alternative therapies

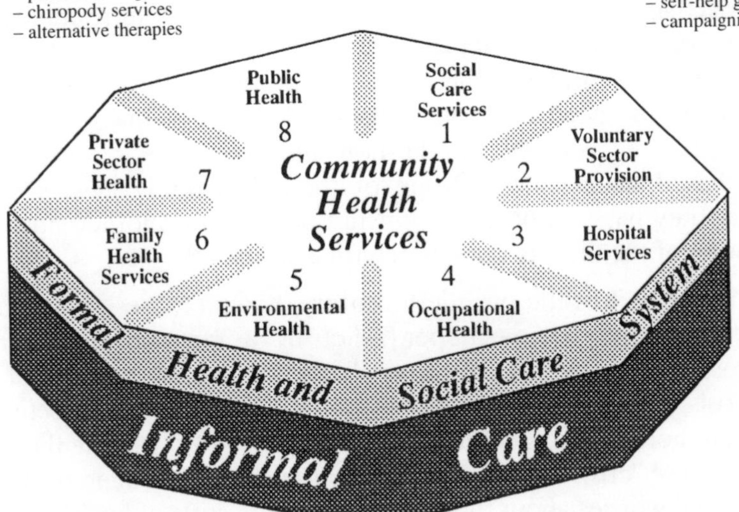

6) ***Examples***
- attachment schemes
- contraception
- dentistry
- health/medical centres
- screening programmes

3) ***Examples***
- hospital at home schemes
- maternity services

5) ***Examples***
- pollution control
- traffic calming

4) ***Examples***
- ergonomics
- stress management

Key: Numbers 1-8 indicate areas of overlap between the community health services and other components of the wider health and social care system.

Figure 1.1

Relations between the various parts of this system are in reality even more complex than indicated in the figure. For service users and providers alike the fragmentation of care has always imposed considerable costs and there have been many calls for more integration. Because of the problems involved, however, it is unlikely that a comprehensively integrated system will emerge in the foreseeable future. Thus, for those with responsibility for the management and delivery of the CHSs, the need to cope with the issues and problems arising from the lack of integration will remain a key concern for many years to come.

At the same time, they must continue to address other issues which arise from the nature of the services themselves. In Ottewill and Wall particular attention was drawn to: the ethical and practical implications of a proactive approach to service delivery; the debate surrounding the relative merits of universality and selectivity; the dilemmas consequent upon increasing professionalisation within the CHSs; the problems arising from the need for more collaboration and teamwork; and the issues associated with decentralisation and the moves towards more locally based management. None of these is entirely new. On the contrary they have all been present in one form or another since the beginnings of the CHSs in the nineteenth century.[5]

In the latter part of the twentieth century, however, these issues have been thrown into even sharper relief by a range of interrelated concerns, many of which have crystallised to such an extent that the term 'crisis' is now frequently used when referring to them collectively.[6] Although there are considerable differences of view regarding the exact nature of the 'crisis', there is general agreement that it is rooted in deep-seated worries about the rapidly escalating costs of health care. In setting the agenda for this book, the 'crisis' and its implications for the CHSs have served as a backdrop.

The 'Crisis in Health'

The expression 'crisis in health' is particularly associated with a variety of concerns which present those responsible for health care, in all industrialised countries, with formidable challenges.[7] Arguably the most significant of these are:

- the questioning of, and even disaffection from, the biomedical or curative approach to health and the search for a broader approach which also takes account of social factors in the definition of health, the determination of health status and intervention;

- the 'epidemiological transition' from a situation in which the major preoccupation was infectious diseases, mainly associated with death in childhood (e.g. diphtheria) and in young adulthood (e.g. complications of childbirth), to one in which chronic and degenerative conditions (e.g. coronary heart disease, strokes, arthritis, Alzheimer's disease), principally associated with old age,[8] are the main concern, together with problems where the situation is deteriorating (e.g. substance abuse, child abuse, accidents, mental health problems, sexually transmitted diseases);
- greater exposure of the 'iceberg' of sickness and disability as surveillance programmes expand and more treatable conditions are detected at the pre-clinical stage (e.g. cervical and breast cancer, hearing defects in children);
- increasing concern about the harmful effects of environmental conditions on the health of groups and communities (e.g. quality of food, pollution);
- the demographic 'time bomb', which is leading to significant changes in the distribution of the population, in particular, a rapid growth in the number of 'very elderly' people, who make greater demands on health care services than those who are middle aged;
- increasing dissatisfaction on the part of users with the quality of health care services and the limited opportunities for them to share responsibility for their health in such a way that the traditional authoritarian relationship between patient and professional gives way to one of partnership;
- a growing appreciation of the fact that inequalities in health care and health status associated with class, gender, race and geography are deep-seated and unacceptable; and
- the widening gap between the demands made on health care services, which appear to be infinite, and the resources, which governments are prepared to make available, to ensure an adequate supply of services.

There is now a convergence of view, amongst commentators operating from very different political and explanatory starting points, that the health care system is in a state of 'crisis'. For the CHSs, with their strong proactive orientation and particular concern for the health needs of vulnerable groups, the 'crisis' is of particular significance. In the sections which follow, each aspect of the 'crisis' is examined, in a little more detail, from the perspective of the CHSs.

The Biomedical and Social Approaches to Health

At first sight the increasing awareness that health and health care need to be seen in a wider social context, within which biomedical factors play an important, but limited, part, would appear to enhance the standing of the CHSs. Arguably, they would have much to gain from the development of a more broadly based health care strategy within which acknowledgement is given to the multidimensionality of health[9] and the fact that health status is affected by the interaction between social, psychological and biological factors.[10]

Moreover, the CHSs have an obvious part to play in attempts to address the shortcomings of the biomedical approach. In the main, these derive from: its narrow biological interpretation of the causes of disease; its mechanistic approach to intervention; its leaning towards provider driven services shaped by the clinical autonomy of doctors; and its undue preoccupation with the clinical conditions of individual patients. As a result there is a tendency to neglect a wide range of factors which affect health status (e.g. income, housing, social networks, culture, employment). Advocates of a more inclusive social approach challenge this restricted view and recognise the value of collectivist, as well as individualist, policies in combating ill health. From the point of view of the CHSs, one of the implications of the social approach is that far more attention should be given to disease prevention, health maintenance and promotion, rehabilitation, after-care and counselling; all of which have traditionally had a far higher profile in the CHSs than in the FHSs and HSs.

Indeed, many of the professions with members active in community settings are either based on the precepts of a broader, social approach or have been reassessing their clinical practice to take account of the insights which it provides. Health visiting, for example, derives its rationale from a more inclusive social approach. This can be seen clearly in the four principles of health visiting articulated by the Council for the Education and Training of Health Visitors in 1977, namely: the search for health needs, the stimulation of the awareness of health needs, the influence on policies affecting health and the facilitation of health-enhancing activities.[11] These principles reflect a broader perspective on the nature of health and a commitment to proaction in health care, which lie at the heart of a socially oriented approach. Similarly, other professions, such as chiropody, dietetics, occupational therapy and physiotherapy, which in the past have largely confined their interest to a biomedical approach, are now becoming increasingly involved in health education and promotion. As Lyne and Stone point out:

> *By virtue of their training and professional philosophies* (members of these professions) *are natural health educators and much of the work they do is designed to promote individual and community health.*[12]

Thus, the CHSs are strategically placed to take advantage of any major shift from cure to prevention within the health care system. They could also lay claim to some, at least, of the credit for bringing about a change in the way that health is perceived and to a share of the resources which would be attached to major proactive initiatives, should this shift occur.

However, the view that the standing of the CHSs is likely to be enhanced may be unduly optimistic. Despite the criticisms of the biomedical approach and the attempts to enhance the status of the social approach, the former remains influential within the CHSs and its dominance within the health care system as a whole has not been seriously eroded. Neither is it likely to be. This is due, in part, to the evident contribution which successful medical intervention has made to the health of individuals. It is also due to the fact that such interventions exercise the imagination of health care professionals, policy makers and the public at large, to a far greater extent than the social approach. Moreover, faith in biomedicine has been orchestrated by media coverage of health care issues. Indeed, there is little awareness amongst the general population of the fact that few medical procedures are grounded in rigorous scientific vetting. Finally, reference must be made to the problems surrounding a more social approach. These include the political and technical difficulties involved in translating the laudable principles into practice and in developing a methodology for judging outcomes. As a result, there is a continuing concentration of power and resources in the hands of those who espouse the efficacy of biomedicine and who have vigorously defended their position.

Matters have been made worse by the tendency for some commentators to juxtapose the biomedical and social approaches and to treat biological and social factors as mutually exclusive, with the implication that policy makers have to choose between them. At a time of resource constraint, this is difficult if not impossible. For example, among the more specific reasons given for the failure of chiropodists, dietitians, occupational therapists and physiotherapists to adopt a more socially oriented approach and to be more active in the sphere of health education and promotion are staff shortages; loss of control following the implementation of general management in some districts; feelings of guilt about the time spent 'just talking' to patients on the part of some practitioners; lack of time; and little support from clinical colleagues.[13] For the CHSs, the situation is further complicated by the existence of a natural tension between those functions which derive from the biomedical approach (e.g. post-operative care by district nurses) and those which are justified in terms of the social approach (e.g. health promotion and the advocacy role of the health visitor). As a result of the continuing influence of the biomedical approach and of the problems involved in reconciling it with a social approach, there is a danger that initiatives in the sphere of health education and promotion will not take full account of the insights to be gained from a broader view of the nature of health. For all these reasons, many practitioners are inhibited from accepting in full the policy implications of the social approach.

The 'Epidemiological Transition'

Changes in the pattern of disease and ill health during the twentieh century have been brought about by a wide variety of environmental, social and medical factors.[14] The CHSs have both contributed to, and been affected by, this 'epidemiological transition'. On the one hand, through their involvement with the management and delivery of vaccination and immunisation programmes for children, CHSs staff have made a significant contribution to the reduction in the incidence of potentially fatal childhood diseases, such as diphtheria. On the other hand, with the increasing incidence of chronic and degenerative diseases, many of which are not life threatening, and the improved survival rates for those suffering from conditions such as heart attacks and strokes CHSs staff play an expanding and demanding role in the spheres of rehabilitation and after-care. Similarly, the increasing prominence of mental health problems, disability, accidents and HIV infection/AIDS in the health profile is likely to have significant implications for the CHSs in the future.

Although **mental health problems** are difficult to quantify, it is now generally accepted that they are experienced by a large number of people. Furthermore, the indicators used to measure the extent of mental illness, such as GP consultations and referrals and suicide rates, only hint at the unhappiness of individuals, households and the wider community associated with alcohol and drug abuse, depression and anxiety and stress.[15] In responding to needs arising from the various forms of mental distress, CHSs staff are increasingly in the front line.

For example, depressed mothers may occupy a large amount of the health visitor's time and school nurses may be the first to be called upon in cases of abuse of alcohol by school children.

The increasing amount of physical **disability** is also placing additional demands on the CHSs. Of particular importance in this respect is the growing pressure on occupational therapists, dietitians and physiotherapists to maximise the independence of those with disabilities and enable them to lead as ordinary a life as possible.

From the point of view of the CHSs, **accidents** are of particular concern for three main reasons. First, they account for a significant number of years of life lost and a considerable amount of sickness and disability and in so doing highlight the importance of proactive strategies of health promotion. Second, many of the victims of accidents are children, young people and the 'very elderly' and CHSs staff have particular reponsibilities in respect of these groups.[16] Third, if the number of accidents is to be substantially reduced then preventive initiatives must not be narrowly focussed. Consideration must be given to the non-medical prerequisites for health (e.g. safe play spaces for children, accessible public transport, effective control of alcohol, carefully designed housing, affordable heating, adequate street lighting, pavements in good repair) and to cooperation between agencies, including those responsible for aspects of community health care.

With respect to **HIV infection/AIDS,** the chronic nature of the condition and the likelihood of its extensive spread mean that it is now high on the community health care agenda. In the absence of either a vaccine or a cure, the emphasis has been on preventive strategies. These include primary prevention through the promotion of safer means of sexual expression; secondary prevention through screening programmes; and tertiary prevention through counselling, maintaining fitness to live an ordinary life and protecting against opportunistic infections. Many of these strategies reflect innovative work undertaken in the voluntary sector. They are based on partnership between users, informal carers and professionals and a social rather than biomedical approach. The future of service provision in this area is expected to be complex, but will continue to require a major and imaginative input from users, carers and professionals in the community.[17]

For the future, further demands may well be placed on the CHSs as technological change enables more treatment to be provided in community settings, including the home. At the same time, although many infectious diseases have been brought under control, constant vigilance will be required if this is to remain the position. Furthermore, there is likely to be a sustained interest in the contribution which health promotion can make to health status.

The 'Iceberg' of Sickness and Disability[18]

One important way in which CHSs staff can be said to have had a direct impact on the 'crisis in health' is through their participation in the development and advocacy of screening and surveillance programmes. The main purpose of such programmes is the detection either of diseases at an early stage of their development (e.g. cervical cancer), or of conditions which are likely to give rise to disease (e.g. hypertension). Thus, improvements in their effectiveness and expansion of their coverage will serve only to expose more of the 'iceberg' of sickness and disability. This is clearly desirable from the point of view of those whose otherwise undetected problems will be found and treated. It will, however, inevitably impose additional demands on already overstretched health care services.

As the early history of the school health service amply demonstrates, it is not possible to introduce any screening arrangements without being confronted, sooner or later, by the issue of how to provide treatment for those identified as requiring it.[19] The problems are compounded where, as Hogg has shown, the efficacy and quality control of screening programmes are suspect.[20] Significantly, there now exist well established protocols designed to deal with some of the issues surrounding screening programmes. Many such protocols are based on the World Health Organisation (WHO) guidelines and specifically include the requirement that 'adequate facilities for diagnosis and treatment of any detected abnormalities should be available'.[21] However, little account has been taken of the substantial additional costs involved.

For the CHSs the resource implications of greater exposure of the 'iceberg' are likely to be felt increasingly in the spheres of rehabilitation, after-care and counselling. For example, following the implementation of breast screening for the over-fifties, some health authorities have felt it necessary to establish district nursing follow-up services. In taking initiatives of this kind, CHSs staff are coming to recognise that the benefits of screening need to be balanced against the costs, both financial and social. Arguably they are strategically placed to make the necessary judgements concerning the weightings which should be attached to these costs and benefits and to facilitate the active involvement of both users and informal carers in the process, so that the weightings also reflect their needs and preferences.

Environmental Concerns

It is now generally accepted that, in the past, advances in the health of the public at large were due more to improvements in environmental conditions (e.g. sanitation, housing, safe water supply, food production), than to the development of medical procedures and drug treatments.[22] Moreover, 'the earlier optimism that harmful environmental influences were relatively simple to control has given way to an increasing recognition that the environment is continuously changing - often as a result of human activities - and that many of the changes pose new threats to (the) health' of individuals and communities.[23] Unfortunately, however, this has not prevented policy makers in recent years from undermining the position of those responsible for the delivery of environmental health services and of those promoting the cause of public health (e.g. sale of public utilities, contracting resource base of the environmental health services, failure to invest in sewers). The fact that environmental and public health are now receiving more attention by the government is due, in part, to a number of well publicised incidents in the 1980s, such as the outbreak of food poisoning at the Stanley Royd Hospital, Wakefield in 1984 and Legionnaire's disease at Stafford Royal Infirmary in 1985. It is also due to the development of European Community wide standards which have led to Britain being singled out as 'the dirty man of Europe' and to the impact of major industrial accidents, such as those at Chernobyl and Camelford. The Camelford incident was of particular relevance to the CHSs because contamination of the water supply by aluminium led to fears that there would be an increase in the incidence of Alzheimer's disease.[24]

Many initiatives are now being taken at the international level to tackle this aspect of the 'crisis'. For example, out of the thirty eight Health For All (HFA) targets, approved by the WHO's Regional Committee for Europe in 1984, eight relate to the production of healthy environments and cover 'the monitoring, assessment and control of environmental hazards which pose a threat to human health, including potentially toxic chemicals, radiation, harmful consumer goods and biological agents';[25] water supply; air pollution; food contamination and harmful additives; disposal of hazardous wastes; housing; and health risks at work.[26] Subsequently, in December 1989, the health and environment ministers of the WHO European Region's member states endorsed the European Charter on Environment and Health, which underlined the importance of the environment for the health and well-being of individuals and communities and reinforced the principles on which the HFA strategies are based, such as equity, collaboration and the right to be consulted and participate in decisions on aspects of environmental health.[27] Furthermore, the Charter indicated that health considerations should take precedence over those of trade, an important reversal of the priorities usually associated with policy statements of this kind.

Although CHSs staff are not directly involved with most aspects of environmental health, in view of their front line position within the community and their extensive range of contacts with individuals and groups, they are often the first professionals to become aware of a possible link between ill health and environmental factors, such as vermin infestation and the 'sick building' syndrome. As a result, they have a responsibility for feeding this information into the planning systems of their own and other appropriate agencies.

Not surprisingly, it is health visitors who do most in this respect. As Spray, a founder member of the Radical Health Visitors' Group, pointed out, environmental issues seem 'to be natural political territory for health visitors; an inevitable consequence of their professional concerns.'[28] Moreover, this applies not only to their campaigning role but also to their work with individual households. Thus, Robertson, in a standard text on health visiting practice, indicates that when making a visit, health visitors should take account of the environment (e.g. quality of the infrastructure, state of the property, cleanliness of streets), as well as the general economic and social circumstances in which the household lives.[29] In this way, they are in a better position to provide help and advice on health matters and to play a part in the process of ensuring that through their journal and the Health Visitors' Association (HVA), attention is drawn to those environmental conditions which are a danger to health. For example, extensive coverage has been given to the health care problems arising from high levels of atmospheric pollution, inner city deprivation, inadequate housing and homelessness in *Health Visitor* (the journal of the HVA).[30] Similarly, in a memorandum submitted by the HVA to the House of Commons Social Services Committee during its investigation of *Working for Patients* (1989), concern was expressed over the government's failure to address the 'inter-relationship of public policies across a range of social and economic issues and the health service'. The HVA also drew attention to the fact that where policies inimical to public health had either been initiated, or not challenged effectively, by government departments or agencies, the NHS had had to deal with the consequences, as the problems which had arisen in respect of the fitness of food and water had recently demonstrated.[31]

Even though other health care professions, with members working in community settings, are not as outspoken as health visiting in articulating environmental concerns, it seems likely that, as green issues move up the health agenda, increasing attention will be given to this aspect of their role.

Demographic Trends

One of the major concerns of CHSs managers is the need to assess continuously the implications of changes in the structure of the population for the allocation of resources and delivery of services. These changes affect both the level and nature of demand and the ability of service providers to respond appropriately to the demand. An important concept in this respect is that of the dependency ratio, which is a measure of the relationship between those in paid employment and those who are not, such as children and the retired and it is skewed in the direction of the latter.[32]

The ratio is not expected to change dramatically because the decline in the number of young people is counterbalanced by the increase in the number of elderly people. An examination of the ratio, however, does highlight three particular concerns for CHSs managers. First, there is the substantial growth in the number of 'very elderly' persons living in their own homes, who need access to community based health care services (see Figure 1.2).

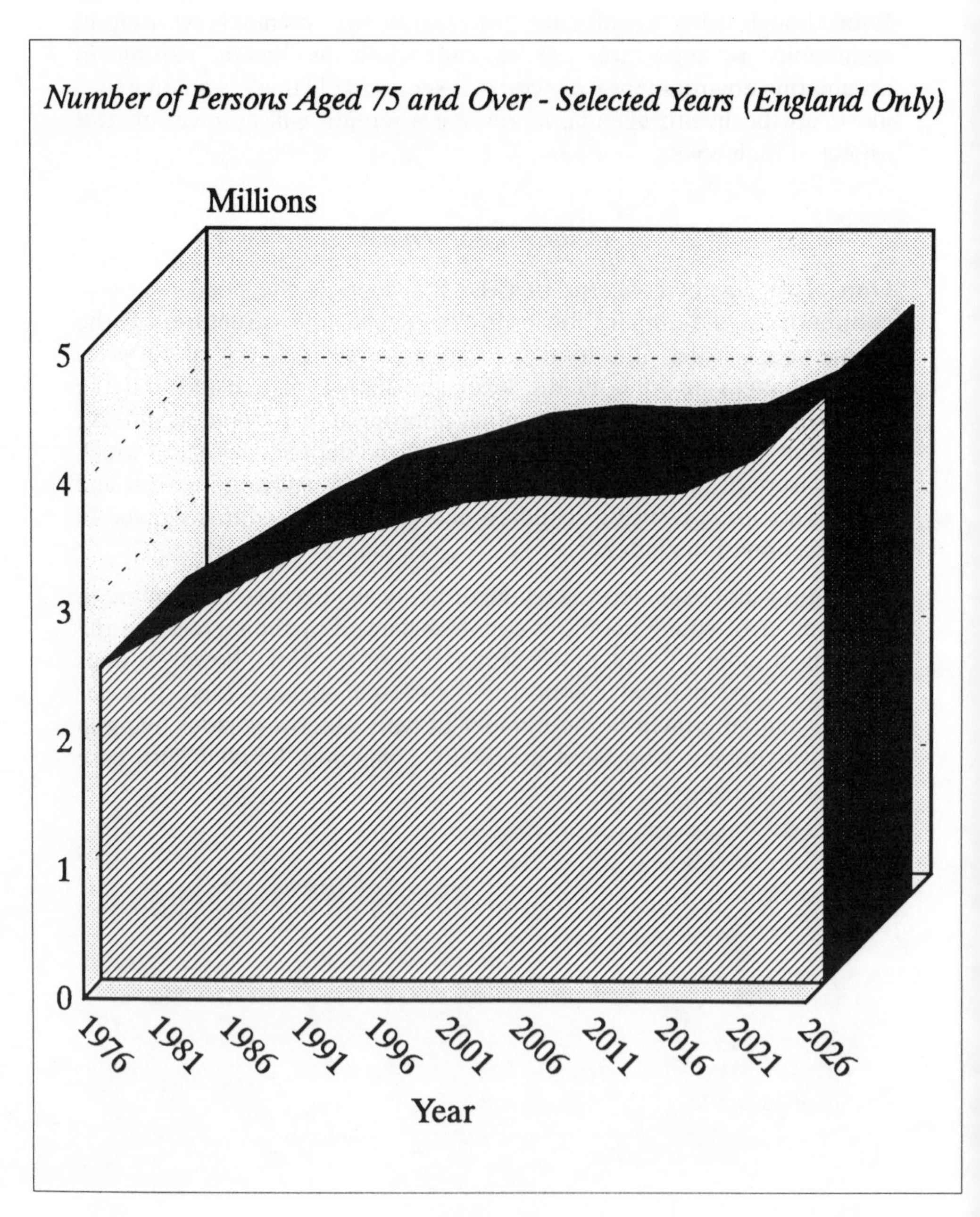

Figure 1.2

Source: Office of Population Censuses and Surveys, *1987 - 2027 Population Projections*, and *Population Trends* (various editions).

Second, the reduction in the number of school leavers will have serious implications for recruitment. Third, socio-economic changes within the population of working age (e.g. in respect of patterns of employment, household composition, gender roles) are having a significant impact on the availability of people to undertake the informal care of their dependent relatives and therefore the nature of the demands being placed on formal carers within the CHSs.

In addition, managers should not forget that general demographic trends can hide important variations within an increasingly heterogeneous population. For example, a number of ethnic minority groups have a larger percentage of children and young people and a smaller percentage of older people than the population as a whole. Such groups have been disadvantaged by managers failing to take account of these differences and making erroneous assumptions about the nature of the family unit within the group, with the result that services for ethnic minority clients have not been sufficiently sensitive to variations in the socio-demographic composition of their districts.

With respect to 'very elderly' people in the population at large, the implications for services generally were addressed in the white paper, *Caring for People* (1989). For those CHSs where they are the principal client group (e.g. district nursing, chiropody, physiotherapy and occupational therapy) the problems faced by managers are likely to be compounded by the changes recommended by the white paper and introduced in the first half of the 1990s. Although responsibility for 'assessing individual need, designing care arrangements and securing their delivery within available resources'[33] now rests with local personal social services authorities, there is still a need for a substantial input from CHSs staff. In the words of the white paper:

> *The Government recognises that achieving the aim of ensuring that more people are looked after in their own homes for a longer period is likely to involve greater demands on the* **community health services** (emphasis added). *Community nursing care, therapy services, and services such as chiropody all have a part to play in enabling people to remain in the community.*[34]

However, although health authorities are 'expected to continue to develop their community health services',[35] they are often being denied the resources to do so. This is evidenced by disturbing reports of cutbacks in out-of-hours district nursing services.

The contribution that CHSs staff could make to community care includes participation in population based needs profiling; assessment procedures for individual clients; the development of care arrangements; and the provision of care in line with contracts prepared by local personal social services authorities. In other words, they have the potential to play an important role within the evolving 'quasi-markets' in health and social care.[36] Whether the potential can be fully realised remains to be seen.

Whatever happens it will be important for CHSs managers to champion the development of services which are designed to promote the interests of service users, to maximise their autonomy and to uphold their dignity. In this way they can help to counteract the unfortunate practice of equating ageing and disability with being a burden.

The decline in the number of young people as a percentage of the population and the consequent recruitment problems challenge CHSs managers to respond in an imaginative and constructive manner. This has involved some movement towards the introduction of more flexible conditions of employment and working practices; efforts to recruit more mature people and those with disabilities; greater use of private sector agencies; and attempts to minimise waste. Recruitment problems have also forced managers to review skill mix and to make increasing use of less well qualified staff.

Similarly, they have been under pressure to adapt to changes in the profile of informal carers and the increasing recognition being given to their needs. For example, in *Caring for People* the point is made that 'assessment of care should always take account of the needs of caring family, friends and neighbours'.[37] In looking for ways of providing practical help to those caring for people who need support in the community, managers should take account of factors such as their gender, age, ethnic origin and other commitments.

It is clear that demographic trends will continue to be a major influence on the planning and delivery of CHSs. Moreover, the changes outlined earlier imply that in attempting to respond positively to the multifaceted needs of 'very elderly' people and other groups, a high priority must be given to the encouragement of collaboration between managers, and of teamwork at the service delivery level, both within the CHSs and across some of the service boundaries identified in Figure 1.1.

Rising Public Expectations

As living standards have improved and members of the public have become better informed, so expectations regarding the quality of both health care services and the relationship between client and service provider have risen. Prompted by the user movement, politicians and health authorities have also played a part in stoking up these expectations with constant references to the importance of consumerism and the rhetoric surrounding the development of customer care and 'personalising the service' initiatives.

Even though these developments affect health services generally, they are of particular relevance for the preventive and promotive services. Because services of this kind are often initiated by the provider they are easier for members of the target group to ignore or reject. Consequently, providers must pay particular attention to the way in which they are presented and to their quality. In so doing, they can ill afford to ignore the wishes and preferences of the public.

For different but equally important reasons, in performing their caring role, CHSs staff need to be particularly sensitive to what clients expect of them. Many voluntary organisations have demonstrated what can be done in terms of good practice and the pursuit of quality in service delivery and have campaigned for higher standards. Members of specialised care groups have insisted on their right to live as ordinary a life as possible. The key to achieving this objective may well lie in service providers recognising:

> *That those who are affected by disability are people first and disabled second and have individual attitudes, likes, aspirations, fears and abilities and understand that although there may be special areas of need, people with disabilities wish to have the opportunity to live the same way as other people.*[38]

Groups representing people with mental health problems, learning difficulties or physical disabilities often argue forcefully that the quality of life available to them is, in general, shaped less by the biological impairments which they experience, than by access to, and power over, the prerequisites of health (e.g. suitable housing, employment, diet, aids and appliances, transport). Young people with HIV infection have been particularly assertive with respect to the standards of care they expect. In taking account of these factors CHSs staff can make a significant contribution to the quality of life of people with disabilities.

Community health projects are another manifestation of the desire on the part of those living in a particular neighbourhood or sharing a common interest to take more responsibility for aspects of their health. The principal aim of these projects is 'to set up a process by which a community defines its own health needs, considers how these needs can be met and decides collectively on priorities for action'.[39] Although many of these projects are not directly linked to the formal mechanisms for the delivery of CHSs, they share certain values with those agencies committed to the development of a more proactive and preventive approach to health care.

Therefore, in view of their proactive bias and their more extensive and closer contact with the community at large, CHSs staff should be at the forefront of attempts to find appropriate responses to rising public expectations and to develop methods for managing and delivering health care services which meet the stated requirements of those who use them.

Inequalities in Health

Although in theory the NHS continues to operate on the principles of equality of access (seeking to offer health care according to need) and equity (aiming to provide equal services for equal need), many studies and surveys have revealed that these principles have been 'undermined by regional, social class, race and gender inequalities, both in health care access and outcome'.[40] A key role in forcing the issue of inequality onto the health care agenda was played by the Black Report.

For the CHSs, there are two main points which need to be made about inequality. First, as was made clear in the Black Report, inequality is even greater in preventive and promotive services than in HSs and FHSs. For example, attention was drawn to evidence which showed that those social groups in greatest need made least use of family planning and maternity services; that working class people made less use of dental services; and that women in classes IV and V were much less likely to be screened for cervical cancer, even though mortality from the disease was much higher in the manual than the non-manual classes.[41]

Second, in order to deal with inequalities in health, Black and his colleagues recommended the development of what they described as a 'comprehensive anti-poverty strategy' with its principal goal being the elimination of child poverty, the severity of which has intensified in recent years.[42] Since the publication of the Black Report attention has been drawn to the fact that low incomes, and the health problems to which they give rise, are not confined to households with children. On the contrary they are closely related to a number of other factors, including age[43] and gender.[44] Thus, any anti-poverty strategy, with improvement in health status as one of its major goals, must take these factors into acount if it is to be effective.

Also included within Black's strategy was the proposal that there should be a shift of resources from hospital to community and preventive services; that urgent attention be given to the needs of people with disabilities; and that a number of 'health development areas' should be designated. This was very much in line with the view that social and economic factors play a major part in determining health status.[45]

Sadly the major findings of the Black Report were not accepted by the government and its recommendations were rejected on the grounds that, at an estimated cost of £2 billion annually, they were too expensive to implement. Thus, not surprisingly, subsequent studies, such as those by Wilkinson[46] and Whitehead,[47] have shown that inequalities not only remain but are also widening. Furthermore, they have drawn attention to inequalities associated with gender, race and geography and the fact that little or no progress had been made towards eradicating them.[48] There has also been a plethora of studies undertaken by feminist and ethnic minority groups investigating aspects of inequality.[49] Unfortunately, however, as a result of cutbacks in the public and voluntary sectors this kind of research has been reduced to a trickle.

The issue of inequality and the question of how best to promote equal opportunities for health were addressed by the Independent Multidisciplinary Committee on the Health of the Nation, chaired by Professor Alwyn Smith. A chapter of the committee's report, *The Nation's Health: A Strategy for the 1990s* is devoted to inequalities in health status. Significantly, Smith and his colleagues supported the view of the Black Committee that, in designing an equal opportunities strategy for health, attention should be given to ways of reversing, amongst other things, the bias towards HSs in favour of community and preventive services.[50]

With regard to the caring aspects of the CHSs, at the time of the Black Committee there was 'little information on class inequalities in the care received by the infirm and disabled'. Moreover, in considering the needs of older infirm people and those who are disabled and chronically sick, the members of the committee found it difficult to distinguish clearly between health care and social care needs and services and argued that, as a result, health care services should not be considered in isolation from other forms of care and support (e.g. social work, meals on wheels, home helps).[51] To a significant extent, this remains the position and it is unlikely to change until full recognition is given to the importance of adequate information and its sharing across administrative boundaries.

At the same time, it is becoming increasingly clear that sexual, gender and racial sterotyping affects the decisions taken by those engaged in community health care and thereby exacerbates inequality. For example, discrimination against gay people, in the delivery of community based services to people with AIDS,[52] has led specialist, hospital based, HIV nurses to worry about transferring responsibility to district nurses when clients require home based care.[53] In order to deal with concerns of this kind, a great deal needs to be done by way of education and training to make staff more aware of the adverse consequences of the discriminatory assumptions which underpin their behaviour.[54] Action also needs to be taken in the sphere of employment policy to ensure that service providers mirror the population served.

Resource Constraints

The continued willingness of governments to fund increases in health care expenditure in line with demographic changes and technological advances is being questioned in all industrialised countries. In this respect, Britain is no exception. Historically Britain has controlled spending on health care more rigorously than elsewhere and consequently spends a smaller percentage of its Gross National Product (GNP) on health than many other countries.[55] Recently a combination of ideological considerations and poor economic performance have led to draconian measures to limit costs. Significantly, however, Britain still sets itself a more demanding agenda in terms of comprehensive provision. For example, with respect to ambulatory care, the UK covers 100% of the costs compared with 98% in France, 92.2% in Germany and 43% in the USA.[56]

Although the resources allocated to the CHSs increased substantially in cash terms between 1974/75 and 1988/89 (i.e. by over 700%), this was from a relatively low base. If allowance is then made for inflation and the additional demands arising from the changing age structure of the population, improvements in the financial position of the CHSs have been even more modest (i.e. increases of 37% and 23% respectively - see Figure 1.3). Moreover, if account is also taken of the quicker throughput of hospital patients resulting in earlier discharge and the implementation of care in the community initiatives, it is probable that there have actually been reductions in service coverage.

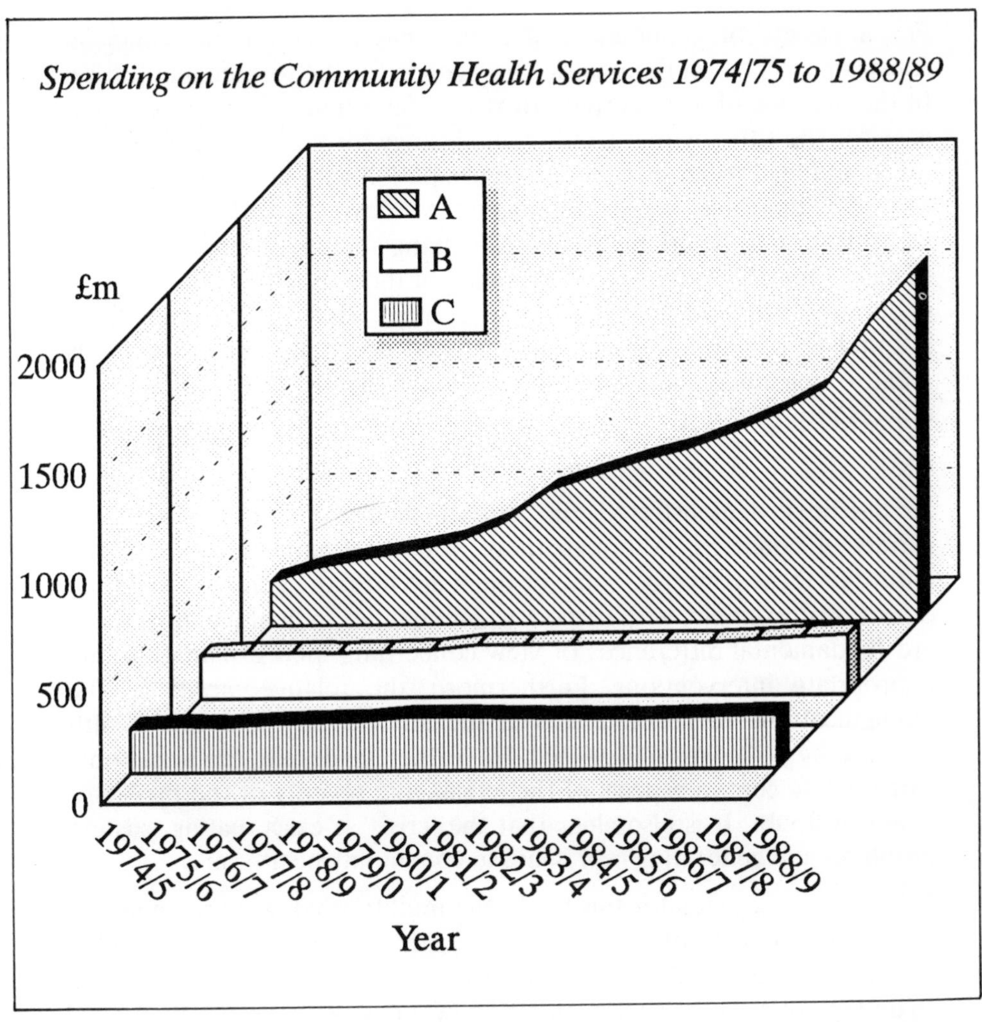

Figure 1.3

Key

A = Spending in cash terms. B = Spending in real terms. C = Spending power after allowance has been made for demographic changes (i.e. numbers aged between 0 and 4 and over 75).

Sources: For spending in cash terms, *Summarised Accounts of Health Authorities etc for Years 1974/75 to 1988/89*, (published as House of Commons Papers). For calculating spending in real terms, The Social Services Committee, *Public Expenditure on Health Matters*, Table 1.6, p.9, House of Commons Paper No.484, Session 1989/90. For demographic data, Office of Population Censuses and Surveys, *Population Projections* (various editions) and *Population Trends* (various editions).

For a variety of economic and social reasons, continuing financial constraint will be on the health care agenda for the foreseeable future. In the absence of a concerted effort to establish an adequate resource base for the CHSs, within a coherent strategy for health care generally, this could lead to an increasing preoccupation with crisis management and less time for service managers to devote to the systematic identification of health needs and to making and operationalising plans to meet them. Continuing underfunding of the NHS as a whole may also undermine attempts to bring about a major shift in resources from hospital to community based services and accentuate moves towards greater selectivity and rationing thus eroding the principle of universality.

As has been demonstrated, the 'crisis in health' encompasses a wide variety of concerns. Although there is general agreement about the nature of these concerns, some of them are far more controversial than others. For example, with respect to inequalities in health status, there are fundamental differences of view concerning their explanation and appropriate interventions. Furthermore, the relative merits of the biomedical and social emphases in the analysis of health and health care are by no means undisputed. Nevertheless, despite the arguments surrounding certain aspects of the 'crisis', the severity of the problems is not in doubt. It is also clear that the 'crisis' is exacerbating existing problems and generating new issues in community health care.

In setting the agenda for this book, the multifaceted, wide ranging and contentious nature of the 'crisis in health' has necessitated a highly selective approach. Moreover, in the space available, it is only possible to undertake a preliminary exploration of the issues chosen.

Agenda Setting

The issues examined in the following chapters are those relating to values, gender, information, planning and commissioning and the 'new' public health movement. Inherent in such an agenda is a desire to consider not only some of the immediate preoccupations of managers and practitioners but also a number of the more far-reaching issues arising from the 'crisis in health', which need to be addressed by the principal stakeholders in the CHSs. Although by no means comprehensive, this agenda does provide a suitably robust framework within which to introduce many of the issues where there is, or should be, a high degree of public, political and professional concern. It is also indicative of the range and variety of issues which confront those responsible for the future development of community health care.

In Chapter 2 some of the ethical issues and moral predicaments associated with the provision of health care services in community settings are examined. Attention is drawn to two key concepts which are employed by those who wrestle with health related conundrums, namely 'personhood' and 'best interest'. These concepts are derived from the ethical traditions of kantianism and benthamite utilitarianism respectively. It is argued that, despite their centrality to informal as well as professional modes of behaviour, they do not yield consistent and unambiguous guidance either separately or together. Moreover, 'personhood' and 'best interest' are shown to be leavened with ingredients from the various groups which make up a culturally diverse society and from the relationships of a market based economy. In other words, they are refracted through the prism of gender, class and race.

It is also contended that within the CHSs there are now a number of constituencies representing different perspectives on values. Three of these are examined namely: the clinical (i.e. doctors, nurses and paramedical staff); the managerial; and the lay (i.e. users and informal carers). The value perspectives of the different constituencies on issues such as resource allocation and multidisciplinary teamwork are outlined. A case is made for redressing the balance of power between the constituencies involved in value laden decision making, thereby ensuring that the process is better informed and more open and explicit.

The principal objective in Chapter 3 is to examine, from the perspective of the CHSs, some of the issues which arise from the increased attention being given to gender in public service provision. More specifically, consideration is given to the roles of women as the major providers and users of the CHSs and as informal carers; to the debate surrounding the position of women in society; and to the impact of the feminist movement on health care. Throughout, emphasis is placed on the implications for the way in which community based health care services are planned, managed and delivered.

Information and the issues surrounding its acquisition, processing, and utilisation by CHSs staff provide the focus for Chapter 4. Attention is drawn to the distinction between formal and informal information and the tendency to concentrate on the former. Discussion centres on the need for and purpose of both types of information within community health care; the relationship between information and behaviour; and the issues of ownership, confidentiality and privacy. The analysis in this chapter is based on the premise that information is not only a key resource but also one which is more complex than is generally assumed. If progress is to be made in developing a coherent strategy for the delivery of community health care, it is argued that serious thought must be given both to information management and to ensuring that informal information is accorded equal legitimacy with formal.

Issues relating to the planning and commissioning of CHSs are addressed in Chapter 5. Priority is given to the debate surrounding the application of the traditional comprehensive or normative approach to planning and the introduction of business planning, which is particularly associated with the move towards a more entrepreneurially based health care system. The chapter ends with a look at the attempts to secure a more integrated approach to the planning of primary and community care services.

In Chapter 6 consideration is given to the impact of the 'new' public health movement on the CHSs. The chapter begins with a discussion of the emergence and main features of the 'new' public health movement and contrasts it with the 'old'. This is followed by an examination of some of the more tangible expressions of the 'new' public health namely: the Acheson recommendations; *The Nation's Health: A Strategy for the 1990s*; the WHO European Strategy; and the green paper, *The Health of the Nation*. Lastly, some of the ways in which the principles of the 'new' public health can be applied to the CHSs are explored and the potential for collaboration between CHSs staff and those committed to the cause of public health is assessed.

Underlying the discussion of issues in Chapters 2 to 6 is the conviction that the CHSs and their staff are well placed to address in a positive and imaginative way many of the challenges arising from the 'crisis in health' and, in so doing, to chart the way ahead. They have a rich and varied vein of traditions, values and methods to tap and are less likely to be constrained by the straitjacket of biomedicine than many of those located elsewhere in the health care system. Thus, what might be termed a **community oriented approach** to health care is seen as offering an effective and efficient response to the 'crisis' and one which preserves the integrity of the principle of equality. In the concluding chapter the principal components of a community oriented approach are identified as well as the prerequisites for its implementation. Potential obstacles and threats are assessed together with those developments which could be interpreted as helpful. On balance it is felt that, despite all the difficulties, the prospects for a move towards a more community oriented approach are relatively good and consequently these are indeed the best of times for the CHSs.

Notes

1 R. Ottewill and A. Wall, *The Growth and Development of the Community Health Services* (Sunderland: Business Education Publishers Ltd, 1990), p.18. The use of the word 'personal' in this definition was deliberate and was intended to highlight the differences between the CHSs and the environmental and public health services. While much of the work done within the CHSs is increasingly being directed at groups rather than individuals, nonetheless there remains an important distinction between group activities of this kind and the collectivist philosophy which underpins the 'new' public health movement.

2 Ibid., p.13.

3 Ibid., pp.14-8.

4 The CHSs also interact with other spheres of public service provision, including housing, education and recreation.

5 R. Ottewill and A. Wall, op.cit., ch.10.

6 See, for example, S. Iliffe, *Strong Medicine. Health Politics for the Twenty-First Century* (London: Lawrence and Wishart, 1988), in which he refers to 'two interconnected crises within the health service', the first being 'a direct consequence of the economic recession and Conservative attempts to escape from it' and the second being 'a long-term structural crisis of medicine itself, running over decades, and common to the advanced industrial economies of the capitalist world' (p.71). Attention is also drawn to the intensity and wide ranging nature of the crisis in many official publications, such as the Biennial Report of the Director-General of the WHO to the World Health Assembly and to the United Nations, *The Work of WHO 1988-1989* (Geneva: WHO, 1989) and OECD Social Policy Studies, no.7, *Health Care Systems in Transition: the search for efficiency* (Paris: OECD, 1990).

7 Although the material in this book relates primarily to England, since every developed country is experiencing the 'crisis in health', a number of references are made to aspects of health care in other countries and to various international initiatives.

8 For example, according to the Alzheimer's Disease Society, the incidence of this disease rises sharply with age: from 5% of the over 60s to 20% of the over 85s. P. Stockton in 'The Alzheimer's disease epidemic: mental status assessment of elderly people in the US', *Critical Public Health,* 1991, no.2, (Special issue on older people), pp.15-6, expresses concern about the way that the increasing incidence of Alzheimer's disease has been used to make 'doom-laden projections of the future dimensions of the problem as life expectancy increases, and the burden it will impose on the entire population in health care costs ...' and to generate unwarranted worries

about 'the cognitive functioning of the entire elderly population', not least amongst older people themselves.

9 See M. Blaxter, *Health and Lifestyles* (London: Tavistock/Routledge, 1990). Some of the dimensions to which Blaxter refers are: freedom from illness; ability to function; 'reserve' (i.e. an inherent stock of energy); physical and mental fitness; psycho-social condition; social relationships; and behaviour.

10 See M. Stacey, *The Sociology of Health and Healing* (London: Unwin Hyman, 1988), esp. chs.1 and 9, in which she argues that health needs should be seen as socially constructed on a common biological base.

11 Council for the Education and Training of Health Visitors, *An Investigation into the Principles of Health Visiting* (London: Council for the Education and Training of Health Visitors, 1977).

12 P. Lyne and S. Stone, 'Talent Waiting to be Tapped', *The Health Service Journal*, 12 April 1990, pp.550-1.

13 Ibid.

14 For a fuller discussion of changes in the patterns of disease and ill health during the twentieth Century, see T. McKeown, *The Role of Medicine: Dream, Mirage or Nemesis?*, 2nd Edition (Oxford: Basil Blackwell, 1979) and J. Mausner and S. Kramer, *Epidemiology: An introductory text* (London: W. B. Saunders, 1985), esp. pp.253-6. See also K. Jones and G. Moon, *Health, Disease and Society: An introduction to medical geography* (London: Routledge and Kegan Paul, 1987).

15 For example, according to a report from the Royal College of Psychiatrists (1990), over nine million people suffer from abnormal anxiety and fears, such as phobias, sudden and unexpected attacks of panic and continuous worry, at some time in their lives. Moreover, as pointed out by Professor Bruce Pitt, the chairman of the College's Public Education Committee: 'these feelings can have a profound and detrimental effect on a person's life'. See also R. West, *Depression* (London: Office of Health Economics, 1992), in which the economic and social consequences of, and the direct costs of treating, depressive illnesses are discussed.

16 See R. Ottewill and A. Wall, op.cit., for details of the responsibilities of health visitors, district nurses, physiotherapists and other groups of CHSs staff with respect to children, young people and the 'very elderly'.

17 For further information about community based initiatives in respect of HIV infection/AIDS, see P. Aggleton and H. Homans (eds.), *Social Aspects of AIDS* (London: Falmer Press, 1988); P. Aggleton, G. Hart and P. Davies (eds.), *AIDS: Social Representations, Social Practices* (London: Falmer Press, 1989); and P. Aggleton, G. Hart and P. Davies, *AIDS: Responses, Interventions and Care* (London: Falmer Press, 1991).

18 According to S. Israel and G. Teeling-Smith, 'The Submerged Iceberg of Sickness in Society', *Social and Economic Administration*, vol.1, no.1, January 1967, pp.43-56, the term 'iceberg' was first used to describe the

large amount of 'undiagnosed illness in the community as a whole' by the editor of the Lancet in 1963. Today, it is also used to refer to hidden need in relation to disability.

19 For further details of the origins of the school health service, see R. Ottewill and A. Wall, op.cit., esp. ch.2.

20 C. Hogg, *Healthy Change* (London: Socialist Health Association and Ruskin College, 1991).

21 H. Buchan, M. Gray, A. Hill and A. Coulter, 'Preventive Measures', *The Health Service Journal*, 22 February 1990, pp.294-5. For details of the WHO screening guidelines, see J. Wilson and Y. Jugner, *Principles and Practice of Screening for Adults*, WHO Public Health Paper, no.34, 1968.

22 This is due, in part, to the pioneering work of McKeown, who argued that the main influences on health were nutrition, environment and behaviour. For further details, see T. McKeown, op.cit.

23 A. Smith and B. Jacobson (eds.), *The Nation's Health: A Strategy for the 1990s* (London: Health Education Authority, London School of Hygiene and Tropical Medicine and King Edward's Hospital Fund for London, 1988), p.2.

24 For a summary of the implications for health of the Camelford incident, which occurred in July 1988, see article by R. North in *The Independent*, 14 January 1989.

25 Target 19. Adequate machinery for carrying out the monitoring, assessment and control of environmental hazards should have been in place by 1990.

26 The targets are reproduced in full in Chapter 6.

27 WHO, *Environment and Health: The European Charter and Commentary* (Copenhagen: WHO Regional Office for Europe, 1990).

28 J. Spray, 'Greening Health Visiting', *Health Visitor*, vol.63, no.4, April 1990, p.137.

29 C. Robertson, *Health Visiting in Practice* (London: Churchill Livingstone, 1988).

30 See, for example, the following issues of *Health Visitor*, vol.63, no.4, April 1990 and no.6, June 1990. In this context, it is interesting to note that homeless families are one of the groups for which local and health authorities are required to make community care plans.

31 See memorandum submitted by the Health Visitors' Association to the Social Services Committee. See Eighth Report, *Resourcing the National Health Service: The Government's Plans for the Future of the National Health Service*, House of Commons Paper No.214-IV, Session 1988/89.

32 For a fuller discussion of the dependency ratio, see J. Ermisch (Policy Studies Institute), *The Political Economy of Demographic Change* (London: Heinemann Educational Books Ltd, 1983), esp. pp.13-14 and pp.117-20.

33 Department of Health (DH), *Caring for People - Community Care in the Next Decade and Beyond*, Cm 849, (London: HMSO, 1989), para.1.12.

34 Ibid., para.4.14.

35 Ibid., para.4.19.

36 For a fuller discussion of 'quasi-markets', see B. Hudson, 'Quasi-Markets in Health and Social Care in Britain: can the public sector respond?', *Policy and Politics*, vol. 20, no.2, 1992, pp. 131-142.

37 D.H, op.cit, para.1.11.

38 Quoted in E. Bumphrey (ed.), *Occupational therapy in the community* (Cambridge: Woodhead-Faulkner, 1987), p.9, from a report published in 1985 by The Prince of Wales Advisory Group on Disability and entitled *Living Options* (Guidelines for those planning services for people with severe physical disabilities).

39 *Guide to Community Health Projects* (London: Community Health Initiatives Resource Unit National Council for Voluntary Organisations, 1987).

40 A. Leathard, *Health Care Provision: Past, present and future* (London: Chapman and Hall, 1990), pp.183-4.

41 Department of Health and Social Security (DHSS), *Inequalities in Health*, [Black Report] (London: HMSO, 1980), paras. 4.21 to 4.28.

42 For an excellent overview of research in this field, together with recommendations for policy and practice, see C. Blackburn, *Poverty and Health: Working with families* (Buckingham: Open University Press, 1991). Significantly, C. Blackburn is a health visitor. See also C. Oppenheim, *Poverty: The Facts* (London: Child Poverty Action Group, 1990).

43 For a discussion of poverty and old age, see N. Bosanquet and C. Propper, *Elderly Consumers in Britain: Europe's Poor Relations? Charting the grey economy in the 1990s* (London: William, Laing and Buisson, 1989).

44 For 'a review of the evidence relating to the part played by poverty and deprivation - material and social - in determining women's health experience', see S. Payne, *Women, Health and Poverty: An Introduction* (London: Harvester Wheatsheaf, 1991).

45 See S. Macintyre, 'The role of health services in relation to inequalities in health in Europe' in J Fox (ed.), *Health Inequalities in European Countries* (Aldershot: Gower, 1989).

46 R. Wilkinson (ed.), *Class and health: research and longitudinal data* (London: Tavistock, 1986).

47 M. Whitehead, *The Health Divide: Inequalities in health in the 1980s* (London: Health Education Council, 1987).

48 For example, recent studies have shown that tooth decay in five year olds in Scotland, Wales and the North West is twice as high as in parts of the

Home Counties, East Anglia and the West Midlands and that children in the most deprived areas of the Northern Region are more than twice as likely to develop diabetes as their counterparts from the least deprived areas.

49 For a summary of work on gender inequalities in health, see H. Roberts, *Women's Health Counts* (London: Routledge and Kegan Paul, 1990). Examples of studies drawing attention to health inequalities in ethnic minority communities include: J. Bennett, *Afro-Caribbeans and Mental Health* (London: West Lambeth Community Health Council and The Afro-Caribbean Mental Health Association, 1990); J. Beliappa, *Illness or Distress? Alternative models of mental health* (London: Confederation of Indian Organisations (UK), 1991); P. Torkington, *The Racial Politics of Health: A Liverpool Profile* (Liverpool: Merseyside Area Profile Group and Liverpool University, 1983); C. Itzin, 'Asian Elderly in Newham', *Elderly People in the Community* (London: Newham Health Authority, 1986); and S. Fenton, 'Health, Work and Growing Old: The Afro-Caribbean experience', *New Community*, vol.14, no.3, Spring 1988, pp.426-443. A recent initiative in this sphere, which is to be welcomed, is the DH funded SHARE Project whose first publication is R. Balarajan and V. Raleigh, *Perinatal Health and Ethnic Minorities* (London: University of Surrey/King's Fund Centre, 1991). This presents challenges with respect to the provision of community maternity services especially to women from a Pakistani background.

50 A. Smith and B. Jacobson (eds.), op.cit., ch.8.

51 DHSS, op.cit., paras.4.29 and 4.34. In this context, it is also worth noting Tudor-Hart's 'inverse care law'. He argues that 'the quality of all medical care, and particularly GP care, (is) lowest where the needs of the population (are) highest'. See J. Tudor-Hart, *A New Kind of Doctor: the general practitioner's part in the health of the community* (London: Merlin Press, 1988), p.10. and p.269.

52 See J. Crown, 'Planning Services within the NHS', *AIDS: Planning Local Services*, King's Fund Project Paper no.68 (London: King Edward's Hospital Fund for London, 1987).

53 For further details, see J. Newbury, 'HIV resources in community nursing' in S. Pike and E. O'Keefe (eds.) *Comments on Community Nursing to the Tomlinson Enquiry on the Future of London Health Services*, School of Health Studies, Polytechnic of North London, 1992.

54 See, for example, a series of five articles in *The Health Service Journal* on management issues in district nursing, 10 November to 8 December 1988.

55 In 1987 the UK devoted 5.8% of its GNP to health care. The equivalent figure for the USA was 11.1%; Sweden, 8.9%; France, 7.9%; Netherlands, 8.5%; and Canada 8.3%. For full details, see Office of Health Economics, *OHE Compendium of Health Statistics*, 7th Edition (London: OHE, 1989),

Table 2.2(a) 'Health care expenditure expressed as % GNP in selected OECD countries'.

56 For further details of the coverage of the costs of ambulatory care in different countries, see *OECD Data File* (Paris: OECD, 1989), Table 16 'Public coverage against costs of ambulatory care by country: 1960-87'. See also OECD Social Policy Studies, no.7, op.cit., p.114.

CHAPTER 2

Values

The CHSs are an integral part of the NHS, which has a distinctive moral foundation. When the NHS was established, four principles or values were formally recognised, namely: universal availability, equality, comprehensiveness and that services should be free at the point of use. In other words, the NHS is not a morally neutral mechanism. Although each of these four values has been compromised,[1] there remains a general commitment to them. Despite a systematic onslaught on the Welfare State by the New Right, none of the major political parties has openly proposed their abandonment. Inherent, therefore, in the NHS is the notion of health care as a public service, as opposed to a commodity. This is significant for the CHSs where a commitment to the values on which the NHS was founded and to a public service ethos promotes the legitimate interests of both users and front-line providers. In this chapter, issues are explored within the limits set by the founding values of the NHS and throughout the book there is a prescriptive undercurrent in their favour.

A consequence of the 'crisis in health' (see Chapter 1) is an unprecedented willingness to examine a wide variety of issues from an ethical point of view. Pride of place has been given to problems about hospital based clinical encounters.[2] These often arise from the new technologies which allow the extension of life in both directions in neo-natal and intensive care units. Questioning has tended to be concerned with biomedical encounters between individuals, usually doctor and patient. Less attention has been given to the complex and subtle value issues emerging in community based health encounters, such as those associated with privacy and confidentiality in health screening and the role of the health care professional as a facilitator.[3] The purpose here is to begin to redress the balance.

To this end it is intended to:

- introduce some of the key concepts, derived from kantianism and benthamite utilitarianism, which can be used to guide the making of value laden decisions within the community health care arena, and to refer to two kinds of knowledge which feed into this process, with a view to enriching the discussion of information in Chapter 4;
- consider these concepts from the viewpoints of constituencies which play a central part in community health care, that is the clinical, managerial and lay; and
- examine a number of moral predicaments facing those involved in health encounters in community settings, such as those concerned with the allocation of resources; ensuring that services are accessible and acceptable; multidisciplinary teamwork; and proactive modes of health care.[4]

What emerges is that, even within the framework set by the founding values of the NHS, there is a plurality of views and an increasing number of assertive voices, including those of nurses, managers, users and informal carers. Some of these have been previously marginalised with respect to the formulation of policy. In the interests of applying the principles of equality and equity it is important to ensure that all groups have an opportunity both to state their position regarding the ethical issues involved and to determine what is to be done. In the context of the 'crisis in health', decision making processes should be made more explicit and systematic; should be opened up to a wider range of constituencies; and should take account of the diversity of views within the population at large. Clearly, changes of this kind are not going to be easy to secure.

Ethical Traditions

In seeking to identify moral values relevant to those engaged in the management and delivery of the CHSs, two ethical traditions emerge as worthy of attention. The first of these draws heavily upon the ideas of the eighteenth century philosopher, Kant.[5] At the heart of his moral philosophy is the belief that people should act according to rules which treat others and themselves as ends and never solely as means. According to this tradition, service providers should treat clients and colleagues as capable of making their own choices and should acknowledge that they have the potential for thinking about and judging their situation, are worthy of respect and have rights. Treating a client or colleague as an object, that is, by-passing their active judgement and participation, always requires careful justification. Such beliefs are summed up in the concept of 'personhood'.[6]

The second tradition is utilitarianism as advanced by another eighteenth century philosopher, Bentham.[7] He believed that actions, laws and policies are right if the benefits to which they give rise outweigh the costs involved. Bentham equated benefits with pleasure or happiness and costs with pain. Other utilitarians have interpreted benefits and costs differently.[8] The focus, however, is always on the consequences of policies and actions. Thus, service providers should use their expertise to maximise the beneficial outcomes of their interventions for clients. They should always act in their 'best interest'.

These traditions and the values associated with them have been selected for discussion for a number of reasons. First, the ideas of Kant and Bentham are clearly reflected in the literature on health policy and medical ethics.[9] Second, their ideas have been influential in the formulation of the codes of practice of health care professionals, including those practising in community settings. Third, popular culture, which serves to colour the attitudes of users and informal carers, has been informed, to a significant extent, by these traditions. Fourth, underlying decisions relating to the delivery of health care services is tacit acceptance of beliefs derived from them, such as the evil of pain, the link between science and progress, the equal status of individuals in determining the general interest and the right to be treated as persons. Last, they are useful tools for analysing the ethical stance of the constituencies mentioned earlier and some of the issues encountered in community health care, on many of which there are sharp disagreements.

Before looking at the values and beliefs associated with 'personhood' and 'best interest', a number of general observations about the traditions will be made. These relate to their origins and subsequent development; their individualist and collectivist strands; and their stance with respect to knowledge of human behaviour.

Kantianism and benthamite utilitarianism both emerged from a Judaeo-Christian culture, but are now largely secularised. They are constantly incorporating and casting off assumptions about 'human nature', derived from the social and natural sciences. These assumptions may be about the capacity for altruism, the presence of instincts, the links between 'mind' and 'body' and the nature of rationality. The dynamism and fluidity of the traditions makes them a fertile source of values. It also makes them logically unwieldy and neither provides unambiguous guidelines for behaviour.

The two traditions took as their starting point the individual. At the heart of the concept of 'personhood' is the principle that people are uniquely valuable and they should be treated as ends rather than as means. Similarly, Bentham in determining 'best interest' argued that the only real interests are individual interests. This does not mean, however, that these traditions underpin only individualistic moral standpoints. For example, kantian principles can be used to justify collectivist strategies[10] (such as black awareness programmes) which seek to promote the ability of groups to understand their situation and to take greater control over their environment. There is, however, always the potential for a clash between the judgement of individual members of a group and the will of the group as a whole.

The collectivism of utilitarianism can be seen in the principle of the 'greatest happiness (good) of the greatest number' and in the drive towards social engineering for the collective good, backed by professional expertise. Thus, there are limits on what can be done to further the 'best interest' of individuals.

Within the CHSs, the juxtaposing of individualist and collectivist values is of particular importance. This is due to the tension between services, such as district nursing, which are directed primarily at the individual, and much health promotion, which is justified in terms of the well-being of the community at large.

With respect to knowledge, in both traditions there is a commitment to the application of systematic approaches to the study of human behaviour. Utilitarians favour deterministic explanations. In their view, behaviour is shaped by the environment and the task is to identify causal factors, through observation and the formal recording of events. Utilitarians rely upon 'explicit knowledge' and formal information. Kantians believe that people are capable of making genuine choices and behave according to rules which they impose upon themselves. People may have privileged access to the meaning of their behaviour. Thus, observers who have no such access, can have only an incomplete picture. What people mean by what they do (i.e. their lived experience) is referred to here as 'implicit knowledge'.[11] Consequently, formal information about human behaviour always needs to be supplemented by a subjective or informal account. Explicit and implicit knowledge are both important for the success of health encounters and this is particularly the case for the CHSs (see Chapter 4).

The concept of '**personhood**' is rooted in the sanctity and moral primacy of the individual. This means that, in the case of health care, service users must be seen as thinking and feeling beings and not defined solely in terms of their biomedical conditions. Thus, 'personhood' underpins a 'holistic' approach to health care. Furthermore, no one should be seen as losing his/her separate moral identity as a member of a family, community or organisation. Individuals continue to be responsible for their actions and need to be able to think and speak for themselves. Even when acting as part of a collectivity, there are limits on what can be done to them as service users and what can be required from them as service providers.

'Personhood' involves treating individuals as capable of voluntary action linked to their interpretation of the facts and their understanding of the situation; as able to make morally relevant choices; and as responsible for their own behaviour. As a result professionals must seek to facilitate the competence of users. This means developing their decision making skills and identifying and removing social and psychological obstacles to rational self-determination.

Where a change in behaviour is sought, strategies of this kind are more likely to be effective than top down compulsion, because they engage the meanings that people bring to their actions. For example, patterns of smoking, eating and physical exercise can be changed only by finding out what these mean to specific groups. Even where the effectiveness of compulsion can be demonstrated, through the inculcation of automatic behaviour or enforced compliance (e.g. wearing of seat belts), 'personhood' demands that health promotion strategies should still be based on education, which equips people to exercise independent judgement in new situations.

Similarly, managers should not demand mindless adherence to narrowly defined protocols on the part of professionals. Although this may meet the requirement of the task in hand in the short-term, in so doing it would undermine the capacity of colleagues to apply their implicit knowledge and judgement and thus, in the long-term, would be counterproductive. This capacity is crucial for front-line service providers in identifying opportunities for health promotion in specific encounters and using their experiences to evaluate services and plan for better ones.

Viewed collectively, the concept of 'personhood' provides a basis for community development within localities and for organisational development within provider agencies, where methods of working offer opportunities for users and employees to take moral responsibility both as individuals and as members of groups or teams.[12] This approach treats both lay people and professionals as having valuable implicit knowledge grounded in their lived experience. Although difficult to document, let alone quantify, it is important to find new ways of ensuring that knowledge of this kind informs public policy making.

Holding people responsible for their own acts, either as individuals or as members of a group, is justifiable in most cases. Dilemmas arise, however, in respect of children and those with mental health problems or learning difficulties, with whom providers of health care in community settings have frequent contact. From a kantian point of view, children gradually acquire the capacities and skills necessary for 'personhood' and thus there is a period during which they require careful nurturing from kin or guardians, with assistance and support from providers of CHSs, such as health visitors and school nurses. Throughout this period they have less than full rights. Tensions could arise for CHSs staff who hold this developmental view of 'personhood', if they disagree with parent(s), guardian or the young person about the degree of maturity attained.

In a similar way, issues arise with respect to those with mental health problems or learning difficulties. The assessment of their ability to be rationally self-determining and therefore the conferment of rights are not straightforward, since behaviour cannot always be regarded as a decisive guide to a human being's cognitive faculties. Indeed, the notion of mental impairment is recognised in law by the concept of 'diminished responsibility'.[13] Just as the family or some other sub-set of society is held responsible for helping children to become full persons, a proxy is required to take decisions on behalf of anyone whose capacity for rational self-determination is reduced below a certain threshold.

This, however, is a minefield. The notion of 'personhood' is double-edged. It is used by those who would restrict the rights of people with mental health problems on the grounds that their rationality is limited. It is also invoked by those wishing to promote their rights. The latter see mental health as an area where medical uncertainty, ignorance and prejudice have unjustifiably curtailed the control which clients have over their own lives. There is a wide spectrum of conditions of varying intensity which involve mental distress. Many of these are poorly understood in terms of causation and effective intervention. Many front-line service providers agree with those directly affected, that some of the restrictions on rights have been unwarranted; the legal and medical categories currently used treat people as objects rather than persons; and the knowledge and experiences of those concerned are largely ignored in the planning and provision of services.[14] In these circumstances it is not surprising that quandaries arise in respect of deciding who is mentally impaired, which aspects of their mental functioning are affected, the extent of the impairment and its possible intermittent nature.

In short, with respect to both children and those with mental health problems, there is a constant danger that their cognitive abilities will be underestimated and that their privacy, dignity and autonomy will be unnecessarily circumscribed. When action has to be taken on their behalf, respect for 'personhood' dictates that every effort should be made to identify what the users would have wanted if they could speak for themselves.

In the absence of a family or social network, it can fall to paid workers to deal with these quandaries. As well as having special responsibilities in this respect (e.g. the assessment function of community psychiatric nurses), all CHSs staff might well, through their contribution to services for children and persons with a mental disability, face moral issues of this kind.

Having pointed to two of the admittedly grey areas, namely childhood and mental impairment, in which self-determination may be restricted, it must be stressed that the overwhelming thrust of the concept of 'personhood' is a shift in the lay-professional relationship towards the conferment of rights on, and the empowerment of, users; an emphasis on the qualitative aspects of service provision; the maintenance and enhancement of the dignity of the individual; and a reliance on the users' implicit knowledge to understand their situation. Even in the grey areas, there have been demands for a shift of this kind (e.g. People First, self-advocacy movement, Childline).

By contrast, the belief that it is appropriate for professionals routinely to make decisions on behalf of others is more closely associated with the utilitarian value system and the concept of **'best interest'**. For the utilitarian, human beings seek to pursue their own interests. They engage in what they think will make them happy or from which they will derive benefit and avoid what they think will make them unhappy. The objective is to secure maximum benefit at minimum cost, which involves a continuous, if unconscious, process of calculation.

Four problems arise from the application of this principle. First, people may be mistaken in their calculation. For example, they may not appreciate the potential costs of pleasurable activity (e.g. 'unsafe sex'). Second, they may choose what is immediately attractive and, in so doing, give too little weight to the long-term costs (e.g. teenage smoking). Both of these problems point to a distinction which can be made between benefits as perceived by individuals (i.e. wants) and their 'best interest'. Professionals present themselves as having the expertise to know what is in the 'best interest' of individuals and to take decisions on their behalf. A third problem stems from the belief that neither individuals nor organisations are altruistic. They are largely concerned about the costs and benefits to themselves and may therefore behave in ways which conflict with the interests of others, with the result that there is a failure to maximise the welfare of the community as a whole. Fourth, Bentham noted that the more power people possess, the more likely it is that the pursuit of their interests will seriously damage the interests of others. For example, in seeking to maximise their profits, the directors of a firm manufacturing baby foods might well market them in such a way that it discourages mothers from continuing to breast feed their babies. By the same token, providers could organise services to suit their own interests, rather than those of other health workers or clients. Clinicians tend to be more preoccupied with the first and second of these problems and managers with the third and fourth.

A health strategy based on utilitarian principles needs to take account of all these problems. It would involve controlling behaviour, with the clear objective of promoting the 'best interest' of individuals and groups; applying the principle of the 'greatest happiness of the greatest number'; and operating effective policing arrangements. In so doing, particular importance is attached to the role of experts in defining 'best interest', changing behaviour and surveillance.

The benthamite would try to encourage beneficial behaviour, whether of service users or providers, through the use of incentives (e.g. subsidising the production and consumption of healthy food, performance related pay) and discourage harmful behaviour through the use of deterrent penalties (e.g. making the polluter pay, imposing very high taxes on tobacco and alcohol, operating disciplinary procedures). If incentives and deterrents failed, the benthamite would have no objection, in principle, to compulsion, for improving the health status of the community at large and it would be ruled out only if it was proved to be self-defeating. For example, compulsory screening is acceptable as long as it does not deter people from coming forward. Although participation by those directly affected might be encouraged, this would be motivated by a desire to win their commitment rather than out of regard for their 'personhood'.

In determining the 'greatest happiness of the greatest number', all the costs and benefits attached to individual interests have to be quantified and aggregated, and options considered, to assess the relative costs and benefits. In carrying out these cost-benefit calculations there is a heavy reliance on the systematic surveillance of the population and services. This results in the production of formal information on matters such as geographic and social variations in health status, interventions by staff, overhead costs and outcomes of health encounters. In short, for the utilitarian policy maker, pride of place will be given to explicit knowledge, hard data and formal information (see Chapter 4).

Essential to the utilitarian approach are policing and auditing (e.g. inspection of nursing homes, 'value for money' studies, measuring the effectiveness of health education programmes), without which the consistent application of the principles of 'best interest' and 'greatest happiness of the greatest number' cannot be guaranteed. Even so, these principles are still threatened by a lack of altruism and the unequal distribution of power. Therefore, policing and auditing have to be backed up with systems of accountability and buttressed by freedom of information and these should be most rigorous in monitoring those with the greatest political and economic power.

For service users, the outcome of a utilitarian strategy is an unequal relationship with professionals, since the explicit knowledge of experts acquired through education and training is accorded greater legitimacy than the implicit knowledge of lay people derived from their lived experience. Moreover, the well-being of members of groups who constitute a minority may be sacrificed to the 'greatest happiness of the greatest number'. The result, for those engaged in policy making and service delivery, is a pervasive concern with economic costs and service outcomes; quantification and the collection of formal information; prioritisation; and efficiency.

Not surprisingly, there are tensions not only between the kantian and benthamite utilitarian traditions but also within each. In practice, they tend to coexist, albeit uneasily, with individuals and organisations reflecting both. As analytical tools, however, they can illuminate and inform responsible discussion of issues in community health. The main values and principles associated with 'personhood' and 'best interest', from both an individual and a collective perspective, are shown in Figure 2.1. Examples of their practical application within community health care are also provided.

Values and Policy Guidelines Associated with 'Personhood' and 'Best Interest'

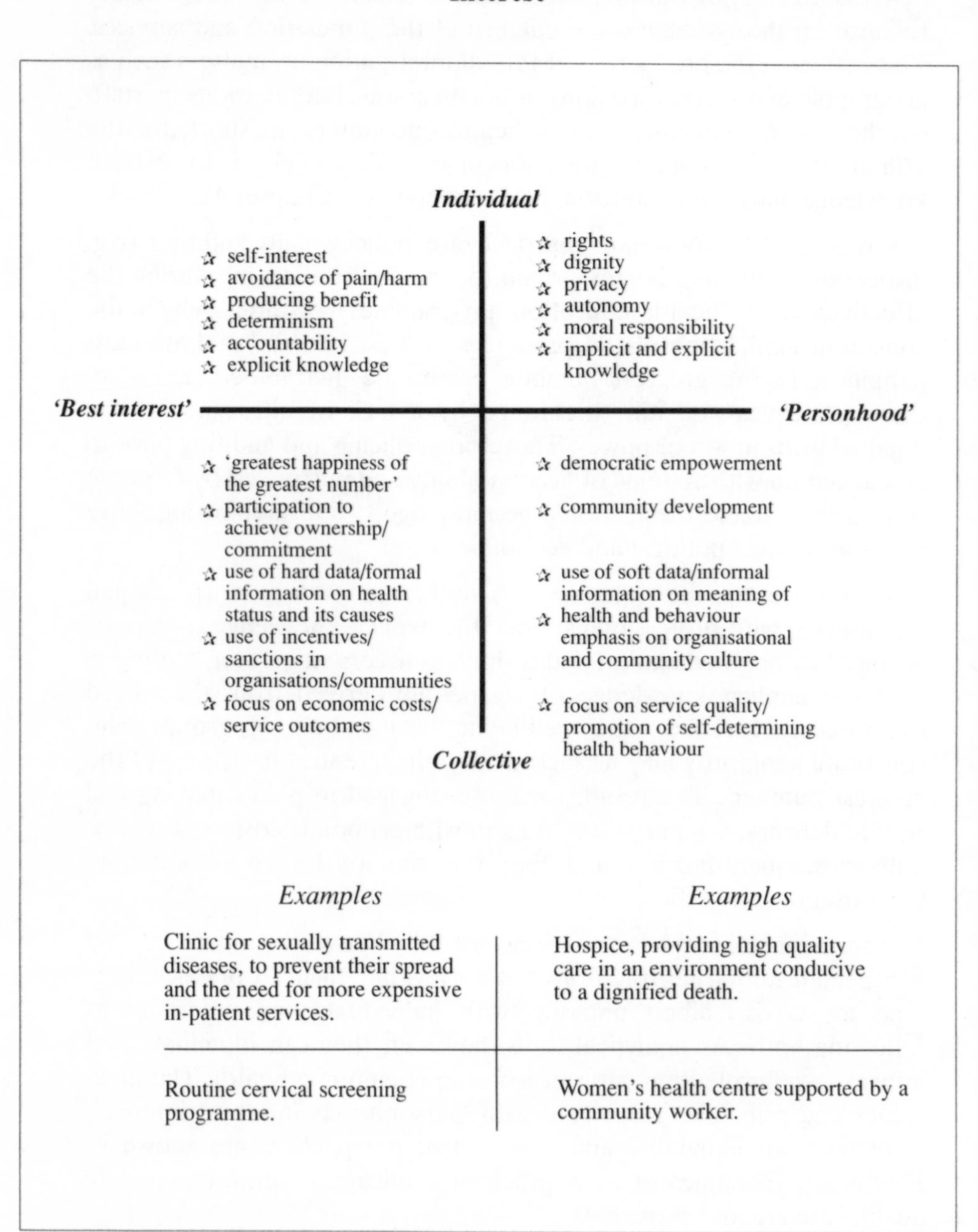

Figure 2.1

Moral consensus is seldom a given in modern societies. This applies even where the disputants are well intentioned and equally well informed. For example, it is difficult to determine whether fluoridation of the water supply is or is not morally legitimate. Where a degree of consensus does exist it is never unassailable. Although few would directly challenge the legitimacy of pursuing a strategy of 'value for money', disagreement surrounds both its importance and the meaning of the word 'value'.

These difficulties are compounded by a number of other factors. First, many ostensibly technical questions relating to service delivery have proved to be difficult to answer because they have a significant moral dimension which has not been recognised. Decisions about the time allowance for visits by a district nurse, for instance, are not value free. They will reflect the extent to which the district nurse and the client are seen as actively negotiating a programme of care, which takes account of the 'personhood' of both parties, and how far the concept of 'best interest' is built into the protocol governing the tasks to be performed.

Second, as Britain has become a multicultural society, ethical traditions, derived from Islam, Hinduism, Rastafarianism, Sikhism, Buddhism, Confucianism and elsewhere have contributed to its value legacy.[15] Within these traditions there are differences of view with regard to moral questions which have a bearing on health. These include questions surrounding sexual behaviour, kinship obligations and the nature of poverty. The intensity of the conflict, to which diversity can give rise, will be greater where those in positions of power share a narrow cultural heritage. The lack of attention to value diversity in service planning and delivery can lead to demands for separate, distinctive provision for minority groups. This offers some guarantee that services will reflect the values of users and service providers from groups which experience discrimination. For example, in certain parts of the country day centres specifically for older members of ethnic minority communities or for those with mental health problems have been established. Although there may always be a place for specialist provision of this kind, value diversity should be a characteristic of mainstream CHSs.

Last, whereas the kantian and the utilitarian recognise the importance of the individual, through the concepts of 'personhood' and 'best interest', in practice people are not accorded equal value. With the increasing detachment of ethics from its religious roots, morality has been reshaped by values derived from the economic system. In the West this has tended to be some form of market economy. As a result, capacity for work, paid employment and economic power are highly valued, and those perceived as 'dependent' are accorded less value than others. This has resulted in a reluctance to allocate money for the support of those who do not work. Indeed, the historic underfunding of the CHSs could well be linked to the low status of many of those who depend on them. Economic inequality is also reflected in the limited extent to which the 'personhood' and 'best interest' of clients served by the CHSs are taken into account in planning and resource allocation.

Faced with this moral labyrinth how should those involved in community health care respond? The 'crisis in health' guarantees that tough decisions, of great moral significance, will have to be taken at every level. This has been recognised by the WHO Regional Committee for Europe. In revising its HFA targets it has recommended that ethical considerations should be 'taken into account in decisions relating to the health of individuals and populations.'[16] In putting this into practice, the concepts of 'personhood' and 'best interest' will help to bring some clarity to the enterprise. It will be necessary to develop methods for ensuring that decisions are taken in a systematic and open manner and in ways which reflect the cultural diversity in society. Only in this way can a sound basis for action be constructed. Ideally, there would emerge from this process a rich and varied pattern of community based health care services.

In practice, there is considerable uniformity in service provision due, in part, to the unequal distribution of power between the constituencies which have an interest in community health care. It is to some of these, and the value positions they hold, that attention is now turned.

Constituencies

With respect to issues in community health care, there is clearly an enormous diversity of interests ranging from large multinational pharmaceutical companies to locally based self-help groups. Moreover, these interests may conflict. For example, while pharamaceutical companies are keen to increase the consumption of their products, self-help groups are often seeking to reduce the drug dependency of their members.

For the purposes of this chapter the following constituencies have been selected for analysis:

- clinical, which can be sub-divided into a number of sub-constituencies based on the following major professional groupings namely: medical, nursing and paramedical;
- managerial; and
- lay, comprising users and informal carers.

Before looking at each in turn, it is necessary to make a number of general points.

First, the taxonomy is not exhaustive. Many other constituencies could have been included, such as: local and national politicians; the private sector; and groups promoting class, ethnic, gender, age and other interests. Indeed, it can be argued that government, both local and national, and business and industry, especially companies producing and marketing food, tobacco, alcohol, military equipment, automobiles and pharamaceutical products constitute the most powerful constituencies influencing health. Such a claim underpins much of the discussion in Chapter 6 on the 'new' public health. The intention here, however, is to examine the constituencies which directly come into play in the planning and delivery of CHSs.

Second, the constituencies are not mutually exclusive, since individuals could well be members of more than one, thereby adding to the value tensions which people often experience.

Third, there are cleavages within each constituency. Nonetheless, there is sufficient common ground, arising from similarities in the position, education, social background and occupational socialisation of clinicians and managers and in the experiences which lay people have as service users, to justify this taxonomy.

Fourth, those who present themselves as most competent to pronounce on moral issues are health care professionals. Not surprisingly, far more has been written on medical and nursing ethics and, more recently the ethics of paramedical professions, than the values espoused by the other constituencies. This is unfortunate and it is therefore intended to give equal attention to each constituency.

Last, the balance of power between the constituencies is subject to change. Since the early 1980s, the hegemony of the medical sub-constituency has been challenged by the government through the strengthening of the managerial constituency. Consequently, doctors and managers are in competition with one another for primacy in shaping health policy. Similarly, even though the lay constituency has been traditionally weak, with the advent of consumerism, its position can no longer be ignored.

Clinical Constituency

The defining characteristic of this constituency is the concept of professionalism. Professions are organised occupational groups held in high social esteem. The work of health professionals is intimately bound up with personal welfare and their skills and specialist knowledge derive from 'science' based training. Members of clinical professions are obliged to enter 'dangerous ground' where the ordinary boundaries of bodily, psychic or social integrity are breached. In the clinical encounter the client is relatively vulnerable and the professional relatively powerful. The client may not be in a position to be self-determining or rational (at least temporarily) and needs to be assured that practitioners can be trusted to act in the way that the user would have chosen (i.e. 'personhood') or in the user's 'best interest'.

The ethical issues to which the clinical constituency gives a high priority are those which arise from the one-to-one interaction between professional and client. Thus, the codes of conduct, which regulate the behaviour of members of the clinical professions, place particular emphasis on the individual, as opposed to the collective, well-being of clients/patients. In addition, the 'best interest', rather than the 'personhood', of clients is seen as the prime, but not the exclusive, concern of health professionals (see Figure 2.2).

Extracts from Codes of Conduct for Clinical Professions with Members Practising in Community Settings

Code of Professional Conduct for the Nurse Midwife and Health Visitor

'Each registered nurse, midwife and health visitor is accountable for his or her practice, and, in the exercise of professional accountability shall:

... Act always in such a way as to promote and safeguard the well being and interests of patients/clients.'

The College of Speech Therapists: Code of Ethics and Professional Conduct

'The primary professional obligation for all speech therapists is to the long term welfare of their patients.'

Rules of Professional Conduct for Physiotherapists

'Chartered physiotherapists shall confine themselves to clinical diagnosis and practice in those fields of physiotherapy in which they have been trained and which are recognised by the profession to be beneficial'

'This rule incorporates the ethical principle defining the relationship between Chartered physiotherapists and patients, i.e. Chartered physiotherapists should always aim to benefit patients through the exercise of their professional knowledge and skills acquired through training and experience.'

British Association of Occupational Therapists : Code of Professional Conduct

Statement:

'Occupational therapists must acknowledge the boundaries of their competence and the limit of their experience. They should only provide services and use techniques for which they are qualified by training and experience.'

Notes:

'... Occupational therapists should refrain from undertaking any activity in which problems or conflicts of a personal nature are likely to affect their competence or cause harm to patients, clients or colleagues.'

Figure 2.2

Nothing in these codes actually prohibits either collectivist developments in professional practice or greater emphasis being placed on the 'personhood' of clients. Indeed, health visiting and public health medicine have always had a strong collective orientation. However, for the most influential professionals, individual clients are the central focus of their work. With respect to the CHSs this is unfortunate. Although it is essential to hold onto 'best interest' as a guide for the delivery of services to specific individuals, it is not sufficient to underpin either services directed at a given population or those which involve counselling and support. A great deal of health promotion, for example, must be justified in collectivist terms and central to most caring activities is the notion of 'personhood'. The dominant values and prevailing climate within the clinical constituency do not provide the most fertile environment for the CHSs.

In recent years, the greater willingness to ask fundamental questions has thrown into sharper relief a number of issues for professionals. Arguably, the debate which this has generated may serve to strengthen the position of the CHSs within the health and social care system.

First, there is, at the heart of professionalism,[17] a paradox. In promoting their own 'personhood', professionals may unwittingly damage that of service users through the creation of dependency. Any attempt to reverse this and enhance the 'personhood' of service users would be in the interests of the CHSs (see Chapter 7).[18]

Second, tension exists where professionals have to balance the well-being of individual clients with the need to ration resources. This is a result of the increasing involvement of professionals in resource management. In such a situation, it is clear that the user's confidence in the service provider may be undermined. Where the ability of the professional to act in the 'best interest' of the client is threatened by underfunding, clear statements about the level of services that users can expect, rather than provider-led decisions which may be discriminatory, could offer a way forward. Application of the principles of partnership and community participation, which are needed to ensure the equity and acceptability of these statements, are particularly associated with the CHSs.

Last, a slightly different issue relates to the need for members of different professions to work together in the 'best interest' of service users. This is of particular importance in community settings.[19] Given the multi-causality of health problems, teamwork is necessary to ensure that a wider range of skills and perspectives is applied. The case for teamwork is reinforced by the clinical uncertainty which derives from the absence of a strong scientific foundation for many medical decisions.[20] However, the ideal of a team of equals is rarely achieved and consequently the 'personhood' of some members of the team (e.g. nurses) is undermined, while that of others (e.g. doctors) is respected. As a result, the contribution which some members could make is wasted. This is likely to be less acceptable in the future and any moves towards greater equality amongst professionals will benefit those involved in community health care (see Chapter 3).

Having considered the clinical constituency as a whole, it is now necessary to examine ways in which each of the clinical sub-constituencies addresses value questions. Traditionally, the **medical sub-constituency** has dominated the health care scene.[21] Because doctors have been so successful in promoting and protecting their interests, they have served as a role model for other occupational groups seeking professional status. Thus, although the role of doctors within the CHSs has been relatively limited,[22] their influence has been great with respect to both setting the agenda and shaping the moral climate within which decisions are made and services delivered. Consequently, clinical practice, even in community settings, has been influenced more by individualism than collectivism and by the values derived from the concept of 'best interest' than that of 'personhood'. For example, confidentiality has taken precedence over openness with clients; concern for safety over client choice; and a relationship based on compliance over one of partnership.

Unqualified acceptance of medical expertise may be appropriate in an accident and emergency department where the patient is in significant danger and speed is of the essence. In other situations, however, such as those involving gatekeeping, rationing, certification of status, long-term care of patients and the management of primary care services, the values associated with individual 'best interest' are much less appropriate. Here, it is necessary to take account of the 'personhood' of individual patients and to adopt a more collectivist stance. Moreover, a strong case can be made for a wider variety of groups being involved in making decisions of this kind, rather than doctors being in sole control.

Such a case is reinforced by demographic changes and the 'epidemiological transition'. Increasingly, doctors are having to respond to the needs of clients who are either chronically sick or disabled. In cases of this kind it is desirable to supplement notions of cure with a commitment to rehabilitation and the maintenance of health. Encounters are likely to be more effective if doctors seek to engage with the lived experiences of their clients and, in so doing, respect their 'personhood'.

Those committed to community health care need to be at the forefront of the moves towards developing an alternative framework of values. Given the numerical predominance of nurses in the community and the nature of their role, the **nursing sub-constituency** is well placed to open up ethical issues for wider debate. Furthermore, they have experience of developing models of professional practice based on accountability to a number of groups, including themselves, their peers, their own and other professions, their patients, the public at large and their employers.[23] Such models are superior to those of, for example, general practice, where independent contractor status reinforces a notion of accountability which is individualistic or confined to peer review and pays little regard to service users or other professional colleagues.

Historically, nurses have been in a subordinate position vis-a-vis the medical profession, and doctors have displayed a marked unwillingness to share power with them. Consequently, medical values have prevailed in clinical encounters and the 'personhood' of nurses has been compromised through the concept of the 'handmaiden'. Thus, values espoused by nurses, many of which have been grounded in concern for the emotional and social needs of clients, have been marginalised. As has been demonstrated by Smith, emotional labour is a central component of nursing.[24] Thus, it has been less easy for nurses to overlook the 'personhood' of patients, and this has been markedly the case in community settings.

There are signs that the situation is changing. Project 2000, the Cumberlege Report, the emergence of nurse-led units and the development of the nursing process and primary nursing all point towards a growing self-confidence on the part of the nursing sub-constituency. Many nurses are now prepared to challenge the hegemony of medical values and to demand that their competence to exercise independent judgement and to apply distinctive skills be acknowledged. The 'new' nurses are insisting that their 'personhood' as service providers be recognised by their medical colleagues.[25] Significantly, the Director for Professional Conduct of the United Kingdom Central Council for Nursing, Midwifery and Health Visiting has argued that the 1984 Code of Conduct involves a recognition that in nursing 'good conduct is being questioning and challenging and honest and open', which signifies a marked change from the traditional culture based on compliance and submissiveness.[26] Indeed, the preference of GPs for practice nurses, who are generally more submissive, can be seen as a reaction against the growing assertiveness of community nurses based on their new found confidence grounded in the 'rise of nursing science ... and occupational status'.[27]

Whereas it is encouraging that nurses are asserting their 'personhood' vis-a-vis doctors, there is a constant danger that, in so doing, they may inadvertantly damage the 'personhood' of others engaged in the provision of nursing services (e.g. health and social care assistants). These are often less well qualified people, drawn from lower socio-economic and ethnic minority groups. Indeed, nursing has been criticised for its discriminatory practices.[28] If maximum advantage is to be secured from the increasing self-confidence of nurses, every effort must be made to ensure that benefits gained in one part of the service are not at the expense of another.

With respect to users, many nurses are moving from a dependency or compliance model of health encounters towards one based on partnership, in which the 'personhood' of the user is respected. Community nurses, in particular, are 'at the forefront of a campaign to involve people more in their own health care'.[29] This can be explained, in part, by the fact that they are likely to be more aware of the impact of epidemiological and socio-demographic changes. In the case of chronically ill or disabled people, nurses are more able to perceive the drawbacks of a rigid division of labour and over-specialisation, which are amongst the more extreme manifestations of utilitarianism. Despite the difficulties involved, they have shown greater willingness to support the principle of teamwork. Similarly, changes in the roles and expectations of women and the feminist movement have obliged community nurses to rethink their professional practice (see Chapter 3).

Like nurses, members of the **paramedical sub-constituency** are struggling to free themselves from medical domination in terms of both values and practices. Within physiotherapy, for example, the values surrounding the concept of 'personhood' are being more clearly articulated than they have been in the past. Indeed, there are references to them in their Rules of Professional Conduct, alongside those more closely associated with utilitarianism (see Figure 2.2). Rule 2, for example, states that: 'Chartered physiotherapists shall respect the rights, dignity and individual sensibilities of all their patients.'[30] Similarly, under the terms of their code, occupational therapists 'have a responsibility always to promote and protect the dignity, privacy, autonomy ... of all patients with whom they come into contact.'[31] In seeking to develop a philosophy of physiotherapy, Pratt draws attention to both ethical strands which are evident in the profession by suggesting that 'attitudes in ... physiotherapy ... may be single-mindedly scientific on some occasions and comprehensively **person-centred** on others (emphasis added)'.[32]

Despite the differences within the clinical constituency, perceived threats to professional autonomy, exacerbated by the 'crisis in health', have served to narrow these. Of particular concern is the right of professionals to defend the quality of patient care which is seen to be endangered by the scarcity of resources and by increasing managerial control. This includes the right to speak freely; to be critical of government policy; and to highlight shortcomings in service provision where the interests of individual patients are at risk.[33] Nurses have been particularly prominent in this and have been prepared to put their own positions in jeopardy in order to defend the interests of patients.[34] The reaction of managers to this interpretation of professional autonomy is predictably hostile and is often interpreted as special pleading rather than as a genuine concern for patient welfare.[35] Managers have to take a broader view.

Managerial Constituency

Managers are expected to adopt a collectivist stance and are primarily utilitarian in their outlook. Their primary concern is meant to be the 'greatest good of the greatest number'. In pursuing this objective, concern for the well-being of individual clients is not centre stage.

It is their responsibility to promote the 'best interest' of the community at large through organisational efficiency and effectiveness. This means ensuring that the organisation knows what it is doing, that there is strict adherence to budgets and that resources are well managed. In recent years, the attempts to quantify health encounters, for the purposes of appraisal, have made the utilitarianism of managers even more apparent. This is illustrated by the increasing use of techniques, such as the QALY (i.e. quality adjusted life years), which facilitate comparison of outcomes and enable managers to make decisions which represent the 'best' use of resources and balance the interests of different categories of patients in the pursuit of the greater good. In designing and applying these techniques, managers rely on the advice of experts (e.g. public health specialists, health economists), which adds authority and legitimacy to decisions based on such calculations. However, the assessment of both needs and outcomes, which are central components of a utilitarian programme, is underdeveloped and underfunded. In reality, the major preoccupations of managers are economy and cost containment.

The view that utilitarianism can provide the sole frame of reference for managers is rejected by Wall. His rejection is based, in part, on the common criticism of benthamite utilitarianism that, in opting for the 'greatest good of the greatest number', minorities lose out. For him, the notion of equal rights for all users, which owes much to the kantian tradition, is important.[36] Thus, managers have a key role in protecting the rights and promoting the interests of individuals and groups whose welfare may be undervalued in the utilitarian calculation. Consequently, they may well have to defend the interests of vulnerable groups against uncaring families, domination by clinicians and the hostility of local people.

In a similar way, Flynn implies that utilitarianism does not provide a sufficiently robust ethical framework for public sector managers and that they should temper 'best interest' with 'personhood'. In his view, effective management does not rule out the exercise of autonomy on the part of service providers. On the contrary, if organisations are to thrive they must capitalise on the imagination and commitment that autonomy brings.[37] Thus, according to Flynn, the ethics of the managerial constituency should be based on autonomy both for front-line service providers, whose responsibilities require training, judgement and initiative, and for service users who 'should be in control unless there are compelling reasons why they should not.'[38] This 'involves individuals giving up power' and implies an interesting reversal of values where managers can pursue the 'greatest good of the greatest number' by supporting the 'personhood' of users and service providers. However, there is still a basic tension between the value of autonomy which lies at the heart of kantianism and managerial control which underpins utilitarianism.

One practising manager who has sought to address some of these issues is Winkler. She is one of a new breed of manager recruited from the user movement. Her commitment to the 'greatest good of the greatest number' and the rights of users has resulted in a programme for redressing inequality in service provision. In her case the objective is to secure a more equitable distribution of GP services between affluent and deprived areas. A key element of the programme is user involvement in decision-making, with managers being required to earn 'trust and responsibility'.[39] Winkler has stressed the importance of enabling users to participate in clinical matters; of ensuring that they

note 39

have the information they need when using services; and of making sure that they can take a full part in what ought to be a wide public debate on 'funding, priorities and access.'[40]

A strong case can be made for CHSs managers following Winkler's lead and adopting a stance which incorporates both utilitarian and kantian elements. Lay people can usually contribute positively to health encounters and the planning of services if their 'personhood' is engaged. Indeed, without their contribution the effectiveness of services is likely to be limited. It is encouraging that public participation is one of the themes of a series of essays, edited by McNaught and published under the title *Managing Community Health Services*.[41] For providers of CHSs, a high degree of autonomy is essential given both the geographic dispersion of clients and the very divergent nature of the demands made upon them. Where both users and service providers have considerable autonomy, the manager's role may appear to be restricted. In fact, in such a situation managers need to be highly skilled in the arts of diplomacy, negotiation and co-ordination. To this end, managers have sought to enhance their professional status through improved education.

Unlike members of the clinical constituency, managers are not bound by a written code of conduct and ethical considerations still have a lower profile in management than in clinical practice. There are obvious dangers for both clinicians and service users in this state of affairs. Significantly, in 1991, the Department of Health (DH) felt compelled to propose guidelines for the conduct of managers.[42]

Despite the efforts of Flynn, Winkler and McNaught, the autonomy of the user is less well established than that of clinicians and managers. Users, together with informal carers, remain the weakest element of the triumvirate. This has resulted in conflict between managers and members of the clinical constituency over who is in the best position to speak for users. In attempting to undercut the power of clinicians, managers sometimes seek to form selective alliances with members of the lay constituency and in so doing may use the language of user empowerment and self-determination. The fine sounding rhetoric, however, should not be taken at face value, since managers are usually as uncomfortable as professionals with the principle of user power and with genuine attempts to enhance the 'personhood' of those who comprise the lay constituency. Managers and clinicians are equally likely to be self-interested, but would use different ethical positions to justify this. If service users and informal carers are to promote their cause successfully they should not shun alliances with other constituencies but should look primarily to their own resources.

Lay Constituency

For the lay constituency, the major concerns of an ethical nature revolve around the application of 'personhood' to individuals and groups. The failure of utilitarian approaches to take full account of the interests of users and carers in the calculation of 'the greatest good of the greatest number' is also an issue.

One significant consequence of rising public expectations, which is a component of the 'crisis in health' (see Chapter 1), is that service users and informal carers are demanding the right to make informed choices; greater recognition for their contribution to health encounters; and a larger say in the planning and delivery of services. Users are no longer prepared to be treated as passive recipients of services and carers are no longer prepared to be taken for granted. The 'personhood' of both is impaired when community based services are planned on the assumption that unpaid support from relatives and friends will automatically be available (see Chapter 3).

Even though the utilitarian would in principle support the aspirations of users and carers to the extent that they have preferences which should be taken into account when assessing the relative costs and benefits of a particular course of action, the concept of 'best interest' has been used to defend many practices which strike at the very heart of 'personhood'. These have resulted in users and carers being treated as objects; patronised; subjected to research and surveillance without consent; and punished for their lifestyle, sexual behaviour or cultural mores. In expressing their revulsion at abuses of this kind, critics are challenging an underlying premise of utilitarianism, that the expert knows best.

In the past, the dominance of medical culture has meant that members of the **user sub-constituency** have been expected to relinquish their 'personhood', on a voluntary and temporary basis, to professionals, in order to promote their own 'best interest'. However, the restriction on their autonomy was more apparent than real, especially in cases where there was non-compliance with clinical advice. Moreover, their route to a health encounter was often influenced by a lay referral network (i.e. conferring with family and friends about their problem and what they should do about it). Such covert deviance is consistent with a culture which treats users as passive, ignorant and vulnerable. Increasingly, however, users are becoming more overtly assertive and want to have differences of view aired and have clinicians acknowledge that their experiences might be a positive resource, that is, they are seeking to enhance their 'personhood'. This has implications for health care generally, but, for a number of reasons, is of particular relevance for health care services delivered in community settings.

First, service users with long-standing conditions, such as disability and chronic disease, are more likely than those with acute conditions to have implicit knowledge, experience and expertise, relevant to their treatment, which professionals should respect. An important development in this respect is that of users planning for situations in which their competence might be compromised in the future. This has been applied to dying, with living wills;[43] pregnancy and confinement with birth plans; and mental illness with crisis cards.[44] With the growth in the number of domiciliary terminal care teams, moves towards comprehensive community based maternity care and the reliance on community mental health services, initiatives of this kind, which are firmly rooted in the concept of 'personhood', have major implications for CHSs staff.

Second, many of the activities of CHSs staff, such as counselling and health promotion, need to engage users if they are to be effective. Consequently, it is essential to take into account their beliefs and values when decisions are being made.

Third, if professional intervention in community settings is to be successful it must be integrated with users' lifestyles and reflect their value systems. Traditionally services have failed to reflect the diversity of needs, interests and values within the population at large.

A final reason is that, with group work having a higher profile in the CHSs, more attention is being given to ways in which the 'personhood' of individuals can be enhanced through group membership. This involves developing a set of values associated with a collectivist view of 'personhood', such as community development. Ramon, for example, makes a direct link between respect for persons, self-determination and collective empowerment in the context of the normalisation of life for those with mental health problems or a physical disability.[45] She also draws attention to the importance of the experiential or, what is called in this book, implicit knowledge.

Unlike service users, very few members of the **informal carer sub-constituency**, explicitly and knowingly relinquish their 'personhood' either to a professional or to those for whom they care.

What tends to happen is that in some cases the needs of those for whom they care are placed above their own. In other cases, carers define their 'personhood' in a less individualistic way. In so doing, they promote the 'best interest' and/or 'personhood' of those who depend on them. Although many of them do this willingly, others feel compelled or under considerable pressure to make the necessary material and psychological sacrifices. For all carers, there is a very real danger that their 'personhood' will be undermined.

From a utilitarian perspective, it is rare for a comprehensive assessment of the costs and benefits of informal caring to be made. Because of the domestic nature of much of the caring, it can be overlooked. Consequently, managers fail to take full account of the economic, social and emotional costs to the carer and exclude them from decision making. With tight budgets, managers might calculate the minimal resources needed to prevent the breakdown of the caring relationship rather than what carers and users require to have a decent quality of life. The resulting absence of adequate practical support could compound the exploitation and stress which many carers experience.

The ethical stance of informal carers is also affected by their ethnic background,[46] sexual orientation[47] and gender. For example, it is women who are generally expected to provide informal care. As Graham has argued, many women do not adopt an individualist outlook.[48] They are neither the self-interested actors depicted by some utilitarians nor the equally valuable separate beings envisaged by Kant, but act upon more communal interpretations of 'best interest' and 'personhood' (see Chapter 3).

Understandably, many informal carers have sought to retain or regain their 'personhood', both individually and collectively. For some, the value of self-determination is of prime importance. They want the right to choose whether or not to engage in caring activities. This can be a real choice only if there is an adequate infrastructure of health and social care services.

Service users and informal carers together, have the potential to be a formidable force within the health care system. Thus, the lay constituency is being wooed by the managerial and the clinical constituencies. In so doing, it is necessary for both to reassess their utilitarian stance. In the case of managers, their preoccupation with economy and their obligation to pursue the greater good must be tempered by recognition of the 'personhood' of users and carers. Likewise, clinicians have to come to terms with the broader implications of their professional activities and the limits of their expertise.

Nevertheless, there will continue to be fundamental differences within, and between, the three constituencies with respect to the values espoused. Often, however, value conflicts are masked by organisational factors, resource constraints, personality clashes and other considerations. In the next section, a number of moral predicaments, of particular relevance to community health care, are exposed and examined.

Moral Predicaments

The predicaments considered in this section are those associated with:

- the allocation of scarce resources;
- access to services which are equal, acceptable, appropriate and effective;
- multidisciplinary teamwork; and
- proactive modes of health care.

Despite having a contemporary gloss, these predicaments and the questions underlying them are by no means new. Over the years various strategies have been applied, such as resource allocation formulae, administrative mechanisms and organisational change, and there is an understandable faith in the efficacy of problem solving devices of this kind. Nevertheless, it has to be accepted that their success has been limited and that key questions are apparently not capable of being permanently resolved in this way.

It is contended here that part of the explanation is that these predicaments have a significant moral component which has been largely overlooked. Indeed, concentration on the organisational, administrative and technical aspects has actually deflected attention from, and masked, the underlying value issues. Exposing the moral dimensions of health care is only a first step. There will be tensions between those adopting different ethical positions and practical difficulties associated with applying any set of principles. Nevertheless, it is a vital first step. Analysis should precede action and exposure of the ethical nature of many of the central questions in community health care can contribute in an important way to more informed decision making.

In the case of each predicament the intention is to consider some of the moral questions using the concepts of 'personhood' and 'best interest' and the constituencies identified earlier.

Resource Allocation

With respect to predicaments associated with the allocation of resources, two major aspects are of particular concern. First, there are the issues related to the division of resources between community and other health care services. Second, consideration needs to be given to the distribution of resources within the CHSs. Given the increasing constraints on the availability of resources and the need to ensure that they are used as effectively as possible, these have acquired great urgency.

The first set of issues can be expressed in the following terms. On the one hand, resources can be devoted primarily to curative, reactive and medically driven services. Such an approach would be urged in terms of the individualist, utilitarian value of 'best interest' associated with the clinical consitituency, in general, and the medical sub-constituency, in particular. On the other hand, priority can be given to caring, proactive and socially driven services of the kind most appropriately located in community settings. This involves adopting a collectivist stance within either a kantian or a utilitarian frame of reference.

In the past, the power of the clinical constituency has ensured that medically driven, hospital based, services have commanded a disproportionate share of resources at the expense of community based services. This may change. There is a growing recognition that the 'best interest' of individual service users might be better promoted in community settings. This applies not only to chronic illnesses but also to some acute conditions for which 'hospital at home' schemes have been developed. Underlying such moves is growing criticism that hospital based services are expensive and not necessarily effective. This demands a shift of resources from HSs to CHSs.

Moreover, the requirement that agencies responsible for the commissioning of services should do so on the basis of an assessment of the health needs of their populations (see Chapter 5) means that a more collectivist set of values will come to inform the resource allocation process. This will have implications for the CHSs. Where the commissioning process is governed by kantian values this is likely to be reflected in a commitment to need driven community services to which users and informal carers have rights; the implication of which is that the CHSs will receive proportionally more money. By contrast, where a benthamite approach is adopted the opportunity costs of providing community services will be recognised, with the result that hidden economies are likely to be made (e.g. over-reliance on informal carers, minimal choice for users). In other words, even within a collectivist value set, the CHSs will not necessarily benefit from a larger share of resources.

With respect to the distribution of resources within the CHSs, again either individualist or collectivist values can prevail. If decisions are based on individualist values then reactive services and activities, where health encounters usually involve a single user and single provider, such as district nursing, are likely to gain at the expense of proactive services organised on a collective basis.

Within an individualist frame of reference, it is possible to adopt either a utilitarian or kantian stance. With the former, resources would be directed at the task component of encounters and with the latter at the person component. Ideally, a utilitarian approach should involve a full cost-benefit analysis of each task, with attention being given equally to economy, effectiveness and efficiency.[49] In reality, this is not the case. For example, patient care is increasingly being undertaken by cheaper and hence less well qualified staff without reference to evidence about outcome. Put bluntly, effectiveness is being sacrificed on the altar of economy. A kantian stance would result in higher priority being given to the thinking, judging and learning capacities of individuals involved in health encounters and to the relationships between providers and clients. Correspondingly less emphasis would be placed on the tasks. There are two dangers with this approach. First, it is likely that more attention would be given to providers than to clients, with the result that resource allocation would tend to reflect professional priorities rather than client needs. Second, with emphasis being placed on less readily quantifiable aspects of encounters, new methods would need to be established for measuring effectiveness. Neither approach is without its drawbacks and both can be used to justify a particular set of decisions concerning the allocation and use of resources. Therefore, it is important to apply individualist utilitarian and kantian insights to resource allocation. This means, amongst other things, ensuring that efficiency measures are backed up by methods for assessing effectiveness, which take account of the qualitative aspects of health encounters.

Where collectivist values prevail, proactive services, such as screening programmes, and activities involving groups of clients are likely to have a high profile. Nonetheless, predicaments associated with resource allocation remain. For example, respect for 'personhood' could result in a greater proportion of resources being devoted to community development projects, over which the lay constituency has more control. Emphasis on the 'greatest happiness of the greatest number' will result in initiatives, such as those in the sphere of vaccination and immunisation, which imply more power for the managerial constituency.

Resource allocation can never be value free and it highlights the problems arising from the tensions between individualism and collectivism and between the utilitarian and kantian perspectives. These are likely to be more intense within the community sector which embraces a wider variety of modes of health care than hospital services. It is therefore important for those involved to recognise the part which values play and to ensure that they are expressly acknowledged in the making of budgetary decisions. Any attempt to find a value free mechanism for allocating resources is doomed to failure.

Accessibility of Services

Inherent in the desire to secure access to community based services, which are equal, acceptable, appropriate and effective, are moral predicaments resulting from need to balance the 'personhood' of service providers and managers against the 'best interest' and 'personhood' of users. Respect for the 'personhood' of providers involves allowing them some freedom of choice with regard to where and how they practice and to which clients they give priority. This enables them to make greater use of their implicit knowledge and expertise and thereby increase their job satisfaction and sense of worth. Community midwives, for example, have recently been given more autonomy to determine how to allocate time to mothers in the ten days following birth. This is in line with the concept of professionalism which underpins the clinical constituency. However, the managerial and lay constituencies may perceive professional autonomy as threatening their right to define accessibility and it is this which underlies the trend of curtailing the freedom of professionals. For example, community psychiatric nurses are being required to shift their attention to clients with severe mental health problems and away from those experiencing milder forms of mental distress, with whom they feel they can work more effectively.[50] Although the move has been in response to guidelines from the DH, it can be seen as the substitution of a managerial definition of 'best interest' for that of a clinical one and as such is an infringement of professional autonomy. Either way, it has to be recognised that, for certain clients, accessibility will be restricted and thus universality and equality, two of the founding values of the NHS, will be put at risk.

Universality and equality can also be undermined if services are not taken up because they are unacceptable to users. Making services more acceptable involves giving greater weight to the 'personhood' of users and moving towards a partnership between users and clinicians. The objective must be to secure services which are effective from a clinical point of view and acceptable to clients. Although training to improve the communication and facilitation skills of professsionals will make working in partnership with users easier, the underlying tension between effectiveness and acceptability will remain.

The potential for tension will be greater in community settings. This is because, where clients remain in their home environment and in control of their lifestyle, they have greater confidence and are in a position to challenge and to act contrarily to professional advice. Clearly, in so doing there is a danger that their clinical 'best interest' will be undermined. Nevertheless, the emphasis on users as 'customers' encourages them to believe that they, and not the providers, should have the final say in deciding what is to be done. Undoubtedly, in undermining professional authority in this way, the 'personhood' of providers might well be put at risk.

Multidisciplinary Teamwork

For the past thirty years, primary health care has been characterised by efforts to secure multidisciplinary teamwork. A major predicament in this respect is how to preserve the privacy of the user, as enshrined in the concept of 'personhood', and at the same time ensure that professionals from varying disciplinary backgrounds share the knowledge they need to consider collectively what is in the user's 'best interest'. The situation is complicated by the fact that the ethical codes of each professional group underline the importance of confidentiality in its dealings with clients. For example, the *Code of Ethics and Professional Conduct* published by The College of Speech Therapists states that: 'Speech therapists must maintain professional confidentiality with regard to their patients and must refrain from disclosing information about a patient which has been learned directly or indirectly in a professional capacity.'[51]

One way of tackling this problem is for all those delivering care to meet as a team in a structured way and to include the client and the informal carer in the making of clinical decisions. This would mean that confidentiality is vested in the team as a whole. In addition, users would have access to their medical records, a principle which has now been recognised in law. The way forward involves the development of strategies for collective responsibility based on the recognition of the 'personhood' of every participant, professional and lay. Such an approach is consistent with the principles of confidentiality endorsed in government advice on multi-agency care management. According to this advice: 'Information should be used only for the purposes for which it was given ... (and) should be shared on a need to know basis.' Moreover, that relating to users and carers should normally be shared only with their consent and they should be told why and with whom the information concerning them is being shared.[52]

Another predicament associated with teamwork arises from the need to harmonise the activities of members, while continuing to protect their autonomy which is so crucial to professionalism. Clinicians fear that team membership will lead to the blurring of professional boundaries and that they will ultimately lose their exclusive right to use specialist skills.

At the organisational level, the notion of teamwork is also problematic. In the past, the ethical traditions have tended to licence either hierarchies, where the active judgement of subordinates is undervalued and underused, or distinct groups of professionals working in parallel, resulting in a fragmentation of services. Both militate against the 'best interest' of users and are, arguably, not in the long-term interests of the providers.

Unless these value issues are openly acknowledged and addressed progress towards multidisciplinary teamwork within community health care will continue to be painfully slow.

Proactive Health Care

At first sight a proactive mode of health care appears to present more fundamental moral predicaments than a reactive mode. At the level of the individual health encounter reactive care can be seen as morally unproblematic, on the grounds that patients willingly or at ieast knowingly relinquish their 'personhood' so that providers can act in their 'best interest'. Clearly, this is an oversimplification and many ethical issues do arise in encounters of this kind. Morever, when viewed from a collectivist stance and account is taken of the fact that health care is funded out of compulsory taxation, further moral problems become apparent. The principal moral predicament in this respect is the difficulty of distributing care according to need, with the result that neither the 'best interest' of less powerful groups nor the 'greatest good of the greatest number' is promoted. Furthermore, it is by no means uncontroversial that public funds should be used to treat conditions for which organisations could be held responsible (e.g. occupational related illness) or which could be viewed as the victim's own fault (e.g. head injuries to motor cyclists not wearing crash helmets).

While the predicaments associated with a reactive mode have considerable significance for community health care, of even greater import are the distinctive moral predicaments arising from a proactive mode. Whereas people are almost invariably motivated to take steps to obtain relief or help when they are in pain or distress or face imminent death or harm, they are far less likely to take the initiative with respect to health maintenance or symptomless or slow acting diseases. Consequently, provider initiated contacts for illness prevention or health promotion require justification. This is usually done in terms of the 'best interest' of the population as a whole or members of those target groups which are particularly at risk. The objections to proaction tend to fall into two main groups.

First, the scientific grounds on which the proactive strategy is based may be contested with respect to either its effectiveness or its safety or both (e.g. fluoridation, whooping cough vaccination). Moreover, once the evidence on the expected gains from programmes has been assembled, there is always room for debate about acceptable trade-offs between the risks associated with the condition and those associated with the preventive measure. In certain circumstances the collective 'best interest' may be given precedence over individual 'best interest' and 'personhood'.

Second, intrusions on the 'personhood' of those affected by proactive initiatives can cause concern. Some strategies give greater recognition than others to the individualistic version of the concept of 'personhood'. These rely upon making formal information and services available and leave people with freedom to choose their lifestyle. Examples of such strategies include warnings on cigarette packets, advertisements encouraging 'safe sex' and food labelling. A major drawback with this kind of approach is that people are free to disregard the message and continue to behave in what health care professionals consider to be an unhealthy manner. In seeking to overcome this drawback a variety of programmes, involving persuasion and incentives, has been adopted. Even these do not guarantee compliance and can be seen as patronising and as compromising the dignity of those at whom they are directed. Moreover, they can also be criticised for implied 'victim blaming' and for failing to acknowledge the collective obligations of government, companies and other organisations. Similar points can made with respect to voluntary screening programmes and the manner in which they are administered. Their quality can be impaired when they are mechanistic; they do not allow users to raise worries about their health; and the arrangements for feedback and follow-up treatment leave a great deal to be desired.

Compulsion overcomes many of these drawbacks, but in so doing it introduces a new set of moral predicaments. It is a form of social control and may therefore undermine the autonomy of individuals and households. For example, making childhood vaccination and HIV screening of pregnant women compulsory compromises the 'personhood' of those involved.

Proactive modes of health care exemplify, more clearly than any of the other areas considered in this section, the potency of values within the CHSs. With an epidemiological profile skewed towards preventable disease and disability and many conditions resistant to cure, proaction is likely to feature more prominently in the CHSs of the future. Thus, the need to address value conflicts, which are endemic where the initiative lies with service providers, will intensify.

Various attempts, of which those of the WHO are probably the best known, have been made to overcome some of the difficulties arising from the tension between the kantian and utilitarian frames of reference in this sphere. These have informed the 'new' public health movement (see Chapter 6) and have been particularly influential in the construction of a national strategy for health, along the lines of that adopted in Wales and now proposed for England. It seeks to reconcile pursuit of the greater good, so important to the utilitarian, with the empowerment of individuals and communities which is a hallmark of 'personhood'. Thus, the 'new' public health movement can be said to offer a framework of values for proaction in health care, generally, and within the CHSs, in particular.

Whereas there can be reconciliation there can never be resolution of moral predicaments. Thus, some commentators believe that the only way forward is to concentrate on how decisions are made and who makes them, rather than their content.[53] Significantly, the revised HFA target on ethics, mentioned earlier, calls for mechanisms that:

- 'specify and assess the ethical aspects of health policy, health care practice and health research ...';
- 'encourage widespread discussion of consumer and public interests'; and
- 'facilitate open discussion and accountability to the public.'[54]

In other words, the focus is on procedural rather than substantive matters.

The process of choosing and weighing conflicting ethical considerations in a pluralist society should become more deliberate, better informed and open to a wider range of constituencies. This requires the establishment of formal mechanisms at a variety of levels where, through open negotiation, an acceptable answer can be formulated.[55] Some countries, such as the USA and Canada, have already taken the lead at the national level and established ethical commissions.[56] These must be underpinned by bodies at other levels, starting with the locality, to enable members of the lay constituency, along with clinicians and managers, to participate in the process through profiling needs and setting targets.[57] It is at the local level where the links between values and decisions about service provision are felt most sharply.

For such mechanisms to work effectively, they must be buttressed by action on other fronts. First, there should be a commitment to equal opportunities. This involves the imposition of formal rules to ensure that all constituencies are represented on bodies where decisions are made and the allocation of resources to support the weaker constituencies.[58] It also means securing a workforce which reflects more accurately the socio-demographic composition of the community it serves. For example, if ethnic minorities, the working class and women were to be adequately represented amongst managers and clinicians, this diversity of perspective would feed into ethical debate. Underlying a commitment to equal opportunities is the need for those with power to be willing to share it (see Chapter 3).

Second, to ensure that participants are able to contribute, a higher priority must be given to ethical questions within both professional training and the education system more generally. Education and training has the potential to provide those constituencies, whose voice in the past has either been weak or not heard at all, with the competence and confidence to articulate their views on ethical issues in a clear and forceful manner.

Last, the whole process should be shot through with the principles of democracy so that everyone concerned has a right to have their views heard and influence the decisions made.

Together these steps will help to foster: a willingness, on the part of the powerful constituencies, to acknowledge the legitimacy of the positions adopted by others and to accept them as partners in the quest for a workable outcome to value differences; a commitment to rules for ensuring that the interests of the less powerful sub-constituencies are given greater weight and that culturally diverse voices are heard; and an acceptance by those involved of the limits on what can be achieved in this respect.

The challenge is to develop suitably robust procedures for setting and reviewing the moral framework within which decisions on substantive health care issues are taken. These would help to clarify the nature and scope of the CHSs as well as their relationship with other components of the health and social care system and would, almost certainly, lead to their contribution receiving greater recognition. They would also help to bring into the open some of the tensions arising from the uneasy coexistence of kantianism and benthamite utilitarianism and the value conflicts which lie at the heart of some ostensibly technical and organisational problems. By confronting these tensions and conflicts, especially those inherent in community health care, progress can be made towards meeting some of the challenges arising from the 'crisis in health'.

Notes

1 In Chapter 1, for example, reference is made to the fact that inequalities in health status indicate that the principle of equality of access has been undermined and that increasing pressure on resources is likely to accentuate the movement away from the principle of universality. Moreover, comprehensiveness is threatened by current attempts to define 'core services'.

2 The expression 'clinical/health encounter' is used throughout this book to refer to situations in which formal providers (including clinicians) interact with service users, either individually or collectively. It embraces at one extreme, a surgical intervention involving the application of sophisticated technology, and at the other, a health visitor addressing a mother and toddler club on the subject of safety in the home.

3 An honourable exception is R. S. Downie and K. C. Calnan, *Healthy Respect: ethics in health care* (London: Faber, 1987), ch.4.

4 It is important to note, however, that this chapter is not an exercise in philosophy. Rather it draws upon literature from the fields of ethics and epistemology in order to reveal the values which underlie many of the predicaments that masquerade as technical problems and to provide a set of tools for analysing and clarifying them. For an introduction to philosophy and ethics see T. Pateman, *What is Philosophy?* (London: Edward Arnold, 1987); A. O'Hear, *What Philosophy Is* (London: Penguin, 1985); and T. Honderich and M. Burnyeat, *Philosophy As It Is* (London: Penguin, 1979).

5 Immanuel Kant (1724-1804) has been exceptionally influential in shaping modern Western philosophy. His most important work is the *Critique of Pure Reason*.

6 The notion of the 'person', derived from Kant's philosophy, is used extensively in D. Parfitt, *Reasons and Persons* (Oxford: Clarendon Press, 1984). Significantly, R. S. Downie and K. C. Calnan, op.cit., along with many others, regard the notion as fundamental to their consideration of ethical issues in health care.

7 Jeremy Bentham (1748-1832) was not only a philosopher but also an economist, legal theorist and student of politics and government. The most systematic and accessible study of the application of Bentham's ideas to social policy is C. Bahmueller, *The National Charity Company: Jeremy Bentham's Silent Revolution* (London: University of California Press, 1981).

8 For John Stuart Mill, for example, the exercise of liberty was an important component of happiness. See J. S. Mill, *Three Essays: On Liberty, Representative Government, The Subjection of Women* (Oxford: Oxford University Press, 1975). This, of course, was also important for Kant. Thus, Bentham's version of utilitarianism, rather than Mill's, has been used here

for the purposes of analysis, because it provides a starker contrast with kantianism.

9 See, for example, R. Gillon, *Philosophical Medical Ethics* (Chichester, John Wiley and Sons, 1991); R. Rowson, *An Introduction to Ethics for Nurses* (Harrow: Scutari Press, 1990); and D. Seedhouse, *Ethics: The heart of health care* (Chichester, John Wiley and Sons, 1988). See also, L. Doyal and I. Gough, *A Theory of Human Need* (London: Macmillan, 1991), which integrates subtle philosophical argument with social science material on welfare in a very effective manner and includes an extensive discussion of 'physical health and autonomy' as the two basic needs.

10 See, for example, L. Goldmann, *Immanuel Kant* (London: New Left Books, 1971); S. Avineri, *The Social and Political Writings of Karl Marx* (Cambridge: Cambridge University Press, 1968); and A. Jagger, *Feminist Politics and Human Nature* (London: Harvester Press, 1983).

11 See, for example, M. Weber, *The Theory of Social and Economic Organisation* (New York: Free Press, 1947), where human action is defined as 'behaviour when and insofar as the acting individual attaches subjective meaning to it' (p.114). See also, M. Polanyi, *Personal Knowledge* (London: Routledge and Kegan Paul, 1958), who claims that 'into every act of knowing there enters a passionate contribution of the person knowing what is being known, and ... this is no mere imperfection but a vital component of his knowledge' (p.viii).

12 For a discussion of community development initiatives see L. Adams and J. Smythies (eds.), *Community Participation in Health Promotion* (London: Health Education Authority, 1990) and W. Farrant, *Roots and Branches* (Milton Keynes: Open University Press, 1990).

13 For a discussion of the concept of 'diminished responsibility', see L. Field, 'Exoneration of the Mentally Ill', *Journal of Medical Ethics*, no.13, 1987, pp.201-5.

14 See T. Campbell and C. Heginbotham, *Mental Illness: Prejudice, discrimination and the law* (Aldershot: Dartmouth, 1990) and P. Barham and R. Hayward, *From the Mental Patient to the Person* (London: Routledge, 1991).

15 For details of most of these ethical traditions, see R. M. Veatch (ed.), *Cross Cultural Perspectives in Medical Ethics: Readings* (Boston: Jones and Bartlett, 1989) and V. Rispler-Chaim, 'Islamic Medical Ethics in the 20th Century', *Journal of Medical Ethics*, vol.15, no.4, 1989, pp.203-8. Also of interest is L. Afrika, *African Holistic Health* (Maryland: Adesegun, Johnson and Koram, 1989), which was written specifically for use in Western societies. It is based on both the explicit and implicit knowledge of African practitioners and the implicit knowledge of users.

16 WHO Regional Office for Europe, *Updating of the European HFA Targets* (Copenhagen: WHO Regional Office for Europe, 1991).

17 For a fuller discussion of professions and professionalism in the context of community health care, see R. Ottewill and A. Wall, *The Growth and Development of the Community Health Services* (Sunderland: Business Education Publishers, 1990), esp. ch.9. and ch.10, pp.495-500.

18 A good example of a strategy which emphasises the 'personhood' of both provider and user is to be found in C. Hartz, M. Plant and M. Watts, *Alcohol and Health: A handbook for nurses, midwives and health visitors* (London: The Medical Council on Alcoholism, 1990). Here the nurse is depicted as acting as a facilitator and the 'responsibility for recovery is in the hands of the individual problem drinker' (p.31).

19 For a summary of the attempts to apply the principles of teamwork in community settings and the problems involved, see Ottewill and Wall, op.cit., pp.501-3.

20 See, for example, J. McPherson, 'International Differences in Medical Care Practices', *Health Care Systems in Transition* (Paris: OECD, 1990), for a carefully documented account and L. Player, *Medicine and Culture* (London: Gollanz, 1990), for a journalistic account.

21 See, for example, I. Kennedy, *The Unmasking of Medicine* (London: George Allen and Unwin, 1981).

22 For details of the responsibilities of community based clinical medical officers, see Ottewill and Wall, op.cit., pp.460-3.

23 See UKCC, *Exercising Accountability: A UKCC Advisory Document*; B. Dimond, 'Accountability and the Legal Context', *Nursing Standard*, vol.3, issue 49, 2 September 1989, pp.29-30; and C. Johns, 'Accountability and the Practice Nurse', *Practice Nurse*, vol.2, no.7, December 1989, pp.303-4.

24 P. Smith, *The Emotional Labour of Nursing* (London: Macmillan, 1992).

25 See J. Salvage (ed.), *Nurse Practitioners: Working for change in primary health care nursing* (London: King's Fund Centre, 1991).

26 R. Pyne, 'On Being Accountable', *Health Visitor*, vol.61, no.6, June 1988, pp.173-5.

27 D. Wilkin and C. Whitehouse, *General Practice in Five European Countries: Finland, Ireland, Netherlands, Spain, United Kingdom* Centre for Primary Care Research, University of Manchester (Copenhagen: WHO Regional Office for Europe, 1991), p.12.

28 For details of race discrimination in nursing, see D. Carlisle, 'Racism in Nursing', *Nursing Times*, vol.86, no.14, 4 April 1990, pp.24-32, which was the first of a series of articles over a three month period on this topic. See also M. Lee-Cunin, *Daughters of Seacole: a study of black nurses in West Yorkshire* (Batley: West Yorkshire Low Pay Unit, 1989). For details of class discrimination, see M. Stacey, *The Sociology of Health and Healing* (London: Unwin Hyman, 1988), esp. p.93.

29 S. Andrews, 'A Quiet Revolution in the Public Arena: fulfilling nursing potential in the community', *Professional Nurse*, August 1991, pp.684-6.

30 The following commentary on Rule 2 brings out even more clearly the kantian strand within the framework of values governing the behaviour of physiotherapists.

'This rule is intended to define the relationship between Chartered physiotherapists and patients on the basis of mutual trust and respect.
In detail this means that all patients will be treated with courtesy and consideration; they will be informed about and must be given the opportunity to consent to or decline treatment proposals.
Information as to risk and the options of alternative treatment including any warnings of inherent risks in a procedure must take account of the mental, emotional and physical state of the patient.
Failure to warn a patient of the risks inherent in a procedure which is recommended may constitute a failure to respect the patient's right to make his own decision.
The dignity and feelings of the individual patient shall be uppermost in the mind of the Chartered physiotherapist at all times.'

31 British Association of Occupational Therapists, *Code of Professional Conduct*, Statement 6, 'Respecting Patients' and Clients' Rights'.

32 J. Pratt, 'Towards a Philosophy of Physiotherapy', *Physiotherapy*, February 1989, vol.75, no.2, pp.114-20.

33 In reviewing the first national conference on ethics for nurses, held in 1990, T. Turner highlighted the implications of the 'crisis' for nursing in the following terms: 'In the coming months, particularly leading up to April 1991, when all health authorities have to balance their books, the profession should at least examine the question of how it can best support those nurses prepared to stand by moral imperatives when patient care is poor'. See *Nursing Times*, vol.86, no.39.

34 One of the best known examples is Graham Pink. For full details of his case, see D. Brindle, 'The resounding call of the whistleblower', *The Guardian*, 4 July 1990, p.21. See also *Health Matters*, no.12.

35 For example, in 1991 Christine Hancock (General Secretary of the Royal College of Nursing), drew attention to the fact that over the previous five years leaders of management colleges had talked 'about the need to crush professionals' and some general managers had stated that their aim was 'to abolish professional tyranny'. Similarly, a confidential policy paper, *Personnel Policy and Practice*, written by personnel directors in the Trent Health Region, which was leaked to *The Independent* in December 1991, stated that traditional power bases must be broken up in order to end the 'paranoia and posturing' of rival professional groups.

36 See A Wall, *Ethics and the Health Service Manager* (London: King Edward's Hospital Fund for London, 1989), pp.10 and 27-35.

37 Such views are in line with those popularised by T.J. Peters and R.H. Waterman, *In Search of Excellence: Lessons from America's best run companies* (New York: Harper and Row, 1982) and T. J. Peters, *Thriving on Chaos: Handbook for a management revolution* (London: Macmillan, 1988).

38 N. Flynn, *Public Sector Management* (London: Harvester-Wheatsheaf, 1990), p.185.

39 F. Winkler, *Addressing Inequalities* (London: Barking and Havering Family Health Services Authority, 1990).

40 Comments made during a speech to the European Health Care Management Association. Reported in *The Health Service Journal*, 17 October 1991, p.11.

41 A. McNaught (ed.), *Managing Community Health Services* (London: Chapman and Hall, 1991).

42 See H. Gaze, 'Corruption fears spur DoH code for managers', *The Health Service Journal*, 19 September 1991, p.6.

43 See Age Concern, Institute of Gerontology and Centre of Medical Law Ethics Working Party Report, *The Living Will: Consent to treatment at end of life* (London: Edward Arnold, 1988). This specifically ruled out the moral legitimacy of the use of the living will or advance directive, as it is sometimes known, to save money. The alleged benefits of a living will are expressed in the following terms-

'1 An advance directive is an expression of patient autonomy which for some patients is reassuring, should they suffer from serious permanent illness or disability, or terminal illness.
2 Completion of an advance directive may alleviate the fear of unbearable pain ...
3 Discussion between patients and doctors on the use of advance directives will create increased medical awareness of anxieties relating to advanced incurable and terminal disease.
4 So-called defensive, or over-intrusive medical care is likely to be discouraged ...
5 An advance directive may aid doctors and others confronted with the ethical dilemmas of cancer medicine, intensive care medicine, resuscitation and geriatric medicine.
6 An advance directive is likely to reduce the level of stress and distress in a patient's relatives.
7 The arbitrariness of medical decision-making in response to certain ethical dilemmas may be reduced ...'

Examples of model living wills discussed in the report and giving different degrees of guidance to clinicians are presented below.

'If the time comes when I am incapacitated to the point when I can no longer actively take part in decisions for my own life, and am unable to direct my physician as to my own medical care, I request that I be allowed to die and not be kept alive through life-sustaining measures if my condition is deemed irreversible. I do not intend any direct taking of my life, but only that my dying not be unreasonably prolonged.'

'It is my express wish that if I should develop
a brain disease of severe degree, or
b serious brain damage resulting from accidental or other injury or illness, or
c advanced malignant disease,
in which I would be physically unable or mentally incompetent to express my own opinion about accepting or declining treatment, and if two independent physicians conclude that ... my condition is irreversible, then I request that the following points be taken into consideration.

1 Any separate illness (e.g. pneumonia ...) which may threaten my life should not be given active treatment unless it appears to be causing me undue physical suffering. Cardiopulmonary resuscitation should not be used if the existing quality of my life is already seriously impaired.

2 In the course of such an advanced illness, if I should be unable to take food, fluid or medication, I would wish that these should not be given by any artificial means ...

3 If, during any such illness, my condition deteriorates without reversible cause and, as a result, my behaviour becomes violent, noisy, or in other ways degrading, or if I appear to be suffering severe pain, any such symptom should be controlled immediately by appropriate drug treatment, regardless of the consequences ... to the extent allowed by law ...

The object of this declaration is to minimise distress or indignity which I may suffer or create during an incurable illness, and to spare my medical advisers and/or relatives the burden of making difficult decisions on my behalf.'

44 A 'crisis card' published by The International Self Advocacy Alliance in 1989 reads:

For use if I ..... of ..... am involved in a
"MENTAL HEALTH EMERGENCY".

If I appear to anybody to be experiencing "mental health" difficulties that require decisions to be taken either **against my wishes** or **in the absence of my agreement** then I require the following actions to be taken:

A That my nominee, below, be contacted immediately, informed of what is happening and requested to attend as a matter of urgency. My nominee is ...
B. That the following be taken into account ...
C. That the following actions be taken immediately ...

Signed ... Date ...

45 S. Ramon, 'Principles and Conceptual Knowledge', in S. Ramon (ed.), *Beyond Community Care: Normalisation and integration work* (London: MIND Publications/Macmillan, 1991). In the same publication, M. Lawson, 'A Recipient's View', gives British examples of empowerment and self-advocacy modelled on the US and Dutch experiments.

46 See, for example, J. McCalman, *The Forgotten People: Carers in three ethnic minority communities in Southwark* (London: King's Fund Centre, 1990), which stresses the importance of offering health services in 'community centres where carers are in familiar surroundings and community workers can provide assistance' (p.74).

47 See, for example, C. Hicks, *Who Cares* (London: Virago, 1988), esp. chs.8 and 9.

48 H. Graham, 'Behaving well: women's health behaviour in context', in H. Roberts (ed.), *Women's Health Counts* (London: Routledge, 1990).

49 The term 'economy' relates to the costs of the inputs (e.g. staff time) to a clinical encounter and implies that these should be as low as possible. 'Effectiveness' refers to the success or otherwise of the encounter and is therefore concerned with both outputs (e.g. number of clients visited) and outcomes, defined by A. Maynard as 'enhancements in the length and quality of life'. 'Efficiency' is a measure of the relationship between inputs and effectiveness.

50 See E. White and C. Brooker, 'The future of community psychiatric nursing: what might 'The Care Programme Approach' mean for practice and education', *Community Psychiatric Nursing Journal*, December 1990, pp.27-9. See also A. Hamid and M. McCarthy, *Health Trends* 1989, vol.21, pp.67-9, which provides information about community psychiatric nursing support for homeless families and shows that front line workers are able to pick and choose clients.

51 The College of Speech Therapists, *Code of Ethics and Professional Conduct with Ethical Guidelines for Research*, 1988, para.12. The code goes on to state that: 'Where information is shared with professional colleagues or any other person, it is the speech therapist's responsibility to ensure that such people appreciate that the information is being imparted in strict professional confidence' (para.13).

52 DH, Social Services Inspectorate, *Care Management and Assessment Practitioners' Guide* (London: HMSO, 1992).

53 See, for example, E. Gellner, *Thought and Change* (London: Weidenfield and Nicholson, 1964) and A. MacIntyre, *A Short History of Ethics* (London: Routledge and Kegan Paul, 1967).

54 WHO Regional Office for Europe, op.cit., p.63.

55 For an example of what can be achieved through open negotiation, see B. Stocking, B. Jennett and J. Spiby, *Criteria for Change: The history and impact of consensus development conferences in the UK* (London: King's

Fund Centre, 1991). In his introduction, R. Maxwell stresses the value of the conferences as a forum for the consideration of ethical, as well as economic and clinical, issues and the substantial involvement of lay people. Sadly, the government has not been willing, so far, to fund initiatives of this kind. See Chapter 7 for further discussion of these conferences.

56 In the USA, The President's Commission for the Study of Ethical Problems in Medicine and Bio-Medical and Behavioral Research was established 1983. With respect to Canada, for a discussion of nationally produced guidelines relating to research on human subjects, regulation of reproduction, the dying process, organ transplants and AIDS, see B. M. Dickens, 'Current Bioethics Trends in Canada', in S. Scholle Connor and H. Fuenzalida-Puela (eds.), *Bioethics: issues and perspectives* (Washington D.C.: Pan American Health Organisation, 1990).

57 For an example of what can be done in this respect, see R. Dun, *Pictures of Health* (London: West Lambeth Health Authority Priority Services Unit, 1991).

58 With respect to lay constituency, of potential significance are the King's Fund *10 Point Plan for Carers* (see Chapter 3, Figure 3.3) and the TUC Charter for Informal Carers.

CHAPTER 3

Gender

In this chapter gender issues are examined from the perspective of the CHSs. Issues of this kind are usually raised by those who have sought to ensure that due consideration is given to gender in the making of public policies and the delivery of public services. They relate, in the main, to the roles of women and to their subordinate position in relation to men. The decision to include a chapter on gender has been prompted by a number of factors.

First, women play a major part in community health care, as the formal providers of services, as informal carers and as users. They are a force to be reckoned with in all of the constituencies identified in Chapter 2. Nevertheless, traditionally, despite their numerical strength, low priority has been given to both their 'personhood' and their 'best interest', with the result that they have been disadvantaged and services have lacked certain vital ingredients. If community based health care services are to realise their full potential, the needs and aspirations of women must be taken into account. In other words, particular attention should be given to gender when making decisions that affect services of this kind.

Second, the CHSs have been affected, in various ways, by the changing status of women in society. Moreover, despite differences of view regarding the scale and significance of these changes, there can be little doubt that they will play an important part in influencing the future direction taken by the CHSs.

Third, the feminist movement, in general, and the Women's Health Movement (WHM), in particular, have challenged the supremacy of the biomedical approach to health care and advocated a more socially oriented and 'holistic' approach, reflecting the 'personhood' and 'best interest' of women. Indeed, there is a similarity of outlook and an overlap of interest between feminists and those committed to the CHSs, which could be exploited to the benefit of both. Many feminists are attracted to work in the CHSs for this reason.

Underlying all these factors is the increased attention being given to gender inequalities. This poses a particular challenge for the CHSs given that women are far more likely than men to be both providers and service users.

In the sections which follow more detailed consideration is given to the significance of each of these factors and to their implications for the management and delivery of community based health care services. Although there is considerable diversity in the experiences of women, the purpose here is to explore some of the common ground. Moreover, even though some feminists seek radical and fundamental change, the stance adopted in this chapter is a pragmatic one. Major themes are that much can done within existing structures to remedy the unfavourable position of women and that CHSs staff have particular responsibilities in this respect.

Women and Community Health Care

Despite the ubiquity of women within community health care, relatively little attention has been paid to the implications of this quantitative bias for the way in which services are managed and delivered. It is therefore proposed to examine some of the reasons for, and the significance of, the predominance of women as formal providers, informal carers and users. Consideration will also be given to the particular contributions which women make and to their distinctive needs and aspirations. In so doing, some pointers for the future will be discussed.

Formal Providers

Women are traditionally believed to be well suited to a caring role and health care thus appears to be a natural occupational choice. However, for a variety of social, educational and cultural reasons, their options are severely constrained and consequently within health care they are far more likely to be engaged in personal, community based services, and in hospital nursing, rather than scientific and technological activities.[1] Indeed, womens' involvement as paid workers in all areas of the Welfare State including health care has been described as an 'extension of the caring, domestic role women carry out in the home.'[2]

Additionally, some female professionals may be attracted to work in the CHSs as this is one of the few ways in which they can avoid direct control by (male) doctors. For example, district nurses and, to an even greater extent, health visitors have much more day to day autonomy in their work than either hospital or practice nurses. This is even more pronounced in the case of community midwives with respect to their status as practitioners in their own right, by comparison with hospital based midwives.

Consequently, community based professions, such as district nursing, health visiting and speech therapy, are almost exclusively female[3] and in other professions (e.g. medicine, dentistry) female members are much more likely to work in the CHSs than hospitals and general practice. For example, the percentage of female doctors and dentists is far higher in the CHSs than in either the HSs or the FHSs, as Figures 3.1 and 3.2 indicate.

In short, women are overrepresented in health care, as opposed to other occupational areas, but within health care they are more concentrated in the CHSs than elsewhere. As a result, for CHSs to be effective, managers must increasingly take account of the needs and predilections of female employees and give full recognition to the other responsibilities which women either cannot avoid or choose to take on. With the declining numbers of school leavers, which threaten serious staff shortages, failure to do this could have adverse consequences for service delivery.[4] In the past the NHS's record in this respect has been poor. As the Equal Opportunities Commission (EOC) has demonstrated 'high labour turnover and staff shortages are the inevitable consequence of the failure of the NHS to address issues of sex and marital discrimination, and to promote good quality equal opportunities employment practices.'[5]

Thus, if managers wish to secure the future of the CHSs they must enthusiastically embrace recommendations from bodies like the EOC[6] and genuinely tackle the disadvantaged conditions in which women work. This involves the construction and implementation of a programme designed to attract and retain women; to promote their interests; to open up options for them; and to satisfy their ambitions.

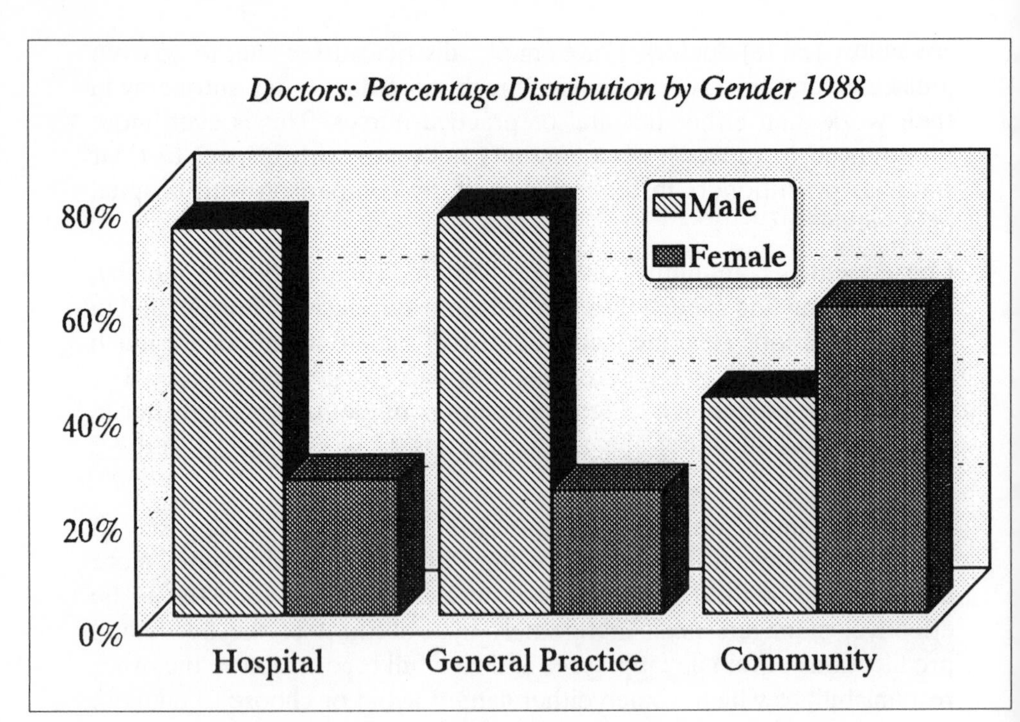

Figure 3.1

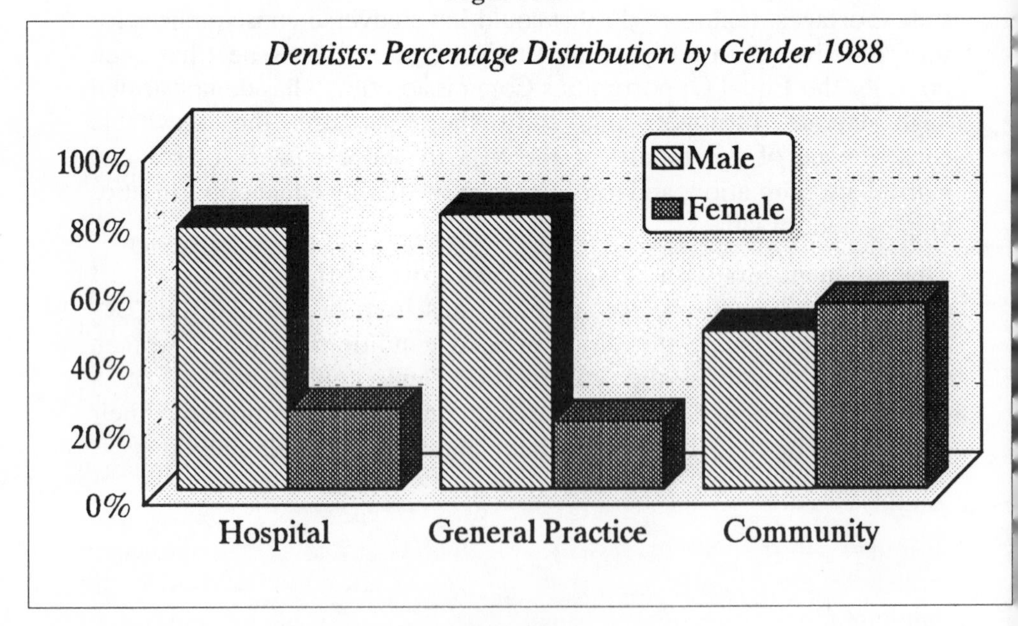

Figure 3.2

Source: DH, *Health and Personal Social Services Statistics for England*, 1990 edition.

As many have argued, the principal components of such a programme must include:

- flexible working arrangements (e.g. job sharing,[7] part-time employment, term-time only working);
- career structures which allow for breaks of service (e.g. maternity, paternity and dependency leave) and facilitate promotion;
- creche facilities and after-school clubs and holiday schemes for school age children;
- childcare allowances and subsidised care for elderly relatives;
- recruitment strategies designed to encourage women to return to paid employment following a break of service, including courses to help women readjust to, and be effective in, the 'public' world;
- application of the principle of 'work of equal value' in the evaluation of jobs for grading purposes;
- non-discriminatory training and retraining opportunities;
- the provision of courses in assertiveness, consciousness raising and confidence building;
- a written policy on the rights of female employees; and
- mechanisms for ensuring that women can participate at every stage of the policy making and implementation process.

Although the legitimacy of a programme of this kind is widely accepted, progress in putting it into practice has been disappointing, especially within health care where moral arguments should carry more sway.

Major deterrents have been the necessity for action on a broad political front and the financial costs involved. However, the costs of not pursuing 'women friendly employment practices' will escalate as the problems of recruiting an adequate number of suitably qualified staff begin to bite. Moreover, evidence is now accumulating of the high costs of staff turnover.[8] Thus, it is essential to adopt a long-term perspective on this issue.

It is also important to recognise that even if the changes in employment policies outlined earlier, backed up by a written code of practice, are implemented, more subtle obstacles are likely to remain. Real, rather than token, improvements in the position of female employees will be secured only when the culture of the organisation is genuinely supportive. CHSs managers, in particular, should be in the vanguard of attempts to find creative and imaginative ways of achieving this end. They should be proactive in seeking to identify and remove sexism; to give higher priority and greater legitimacy to the needs of female employees; and to enable women to fulfil their potential within the workplace. In other words, they should genuinely respect the 'personhood' of women.

Informal Carers

Despite the existence of a wide range of formally provided health and social care services, most caring still takes place on an informal basis.[9] For example, in a study of 'people looking after a sick, handicapped or elderly person', carried out by the Office of Population Censuses and Surveys (OPCS), as part of the General Household Survey, in the mid 1980s, it was found that 'one adult in seven (14%) was providing informal care and one in five households (19%) contained a carer.' Although the study showed that men made an important contribution in this respect, particularly in the care of spouses, a majority of informal carers were female (3.5 million women compared to 2.5 million men) and women 'were also more likely to carry the main responsibility for caring (10% of women and 6% of men).'[10]

This is due, in part, to the fact that the career patterns and low pay of women make it more likely that they will be available to take on responsibilities of this kind. It is also assumed that, by virtue of their femininity, women are better suited to a caring role than men. In other words, women face considerable pressure to accept responsibility for the care of dependents. Moreover, successive governments have added to this pressure by reinforcing, through their social policies, the economic dependence of women on men and the domestic role of women. Consequently, the issue of informal care is of particular importance both for women and for those concerned with the provision of formal services.

Informal carers play a key role in meeting many of the physical and social needs of the elderly and people with a disability and thus reduce the pressure on formal providers and residential services. Their contribution includes attending to matters of feeding and personal hygiene; providing companionship; organising social activities; administering medication; performing basic nursing duties; and acting as a channel of communication between the user and the formal providers (e.g. in respect of the mobilisation of services, making appointments, arranging transport). The nature and extent of the informal caring role will clearly vary from one individual to another and, in some cases, it will be a full time occupation. However, whatever the scale of the commitment, without support of this kind community health care becomes untenable for many people. One of the major implications of the heavy dependence on informal care is that those responsible for managing services should give a high priority to the provision of practical support to carers. In assessing care needs, they should also take full account of the interests and 'personhood' of the carers, whether they be relatives, friends or neighbours and whether they are performing the role willingly or reluctantly.[11] Although practical support of this kind is necessary for all carers, regardless of gender, women do have distinctive needs and problems arising from a number of physical and social factors.[12] Furthermore, there is evidence to suggest that 'gender related assumptions are rife in the community health and social services', and that these result in an allocation of support which is unfavourable to women. For example, district nurses generally expect female informal carers 'to cope better' than males, with the result that 'men cared for by their wives receive less frequent visits'.[13]

In view of the large number of female carers, these issues must be addressed in the interests of securing a fruitful partnership between informal carers and formal providers. The main challenges for CHSs managers, in this respect, are to:

- recognise the distinctive needs and problems of female informal carers (e.g. performing tasks which require considerable physical strength, being expected to give up paid employment to look after a relative) and the gender stereotyping inherent in the way that services are delivered;
- develop non-discriminatory training programmes for both formal providers and informal carers;
- provide male and female carers with equal access to facilities for respite care;
- address the premise often implicit in public policy that home care is necessarily the best;
- ensure that other resources (e.g. staff time, aids and appliances) are allocated according the needs of the users rather than the gender of the informal carer;

- give due attention to *Carers' Needs - A 10 Point Plan for Carers* (see Figure 3.3), which reflects many of the aspirations of the informal carer sub-constituency; and
- set an example to other managers by taking positive action to help their staff who combine paid employment with informal caring to overcome the frustration, guilt and divided loyalties they often feel.[14]

Carers' Needs - A 10 Point Plan For Carers[15]

Carers need:

1. Recognition of their contribution and of their own needs as individuals in their own right
2. Services tailored to their individual circumstances, needs and views through discussions at the time help is being planned
3. Services which reflect an awareness of differing racial, cultural and religious backgrounds and values, equally accessible to carers of every race and ethnic origin
4. Opportunities for a break, both for short spells (an afternoon) and for longer periods (a week or more), to relax and have time to themselves
5. Practical help to lighten the tasks of caring, including domestic help, home adaptations, incontinence services and help with transport
6. Someone to talk to about their own emotional needs, at the outset of caring, while they are caring and when the caring task is over
7. Information about available benefits and services as well as how to cope with the particular condition of the person cared for
8. An income which covers the cost of caring and which does not preclude carers taking employment or sharing care with other people
9. Opportunities to explore alternatives to family care, both for the immediate and long term future
10. Services designed through consultation with carers, at all levels of policy planning

Figure 3.3

In short, managers must take positive steps to apply the principle of 'equal opportunity' to the informal caring role and, in so doing, go some way towards respecting the 'personhood' and promoting the 'best interest' of those concerned. This will become of increasing importance in the years to come because of the demographic changes outlined in Chapter 1. Moreover, the situation will be exacerbated if, as some predict, 'successive cohorts of elderly wives (are) less willing to accept traditional gender based roles'.[16]

Users

As important as the contribution of women to the delivery of formal and informal community health care, is their role as users. Women make far greater use of the CHSs than men. This is self-evident in the case of services designed to meet health care needs associated with their reproductive role, such as ante-natal care, domiciliary midwifery, family planning and cervical cancer screening.[17]

However, even in the case of services which are not apparently related to gender, such as school health, health education and those provided for the elderly, women are more frequently at the 'receiving end' than men. There are many reasons for this and a number of them, which are of particular significance for CHSs staff, are considered below.

First, the position of women within the family means that they are far more likely than men to take responsibility for the health of others. In the words of Graham, 'women ... carry the burden of concern and care for the health of the family.'[18] This applies to the performance of not only their informal caring role, mentioned earlier, but also their general domestic role. One important contribution which women make in this respect is that of mediation between the family and the health services.[19] For example, it is usually mothers who take children to clinics and attend school medical inspections and it is females who encourage male partners to take advantage of screening facilities. A less obvious, but equally important contribution, is the influence which women have on the family's lifestyle. In the main, it is women who shop, cook, arrange leisure activities and determine many aspects of the family's physical environment and thus have the potential to contribute to the maintenance and promotion of health and the prevention of illness.[20] As a result, women are more likely than men to be aware of the impact of broader environmental factors on health.[21]

Second, since women generally live longer than men they are more likely to require formal health services. Given that the incidence of chronic illness and disability, physical and mental, increases with age, old people make considerable use of the CHSs. The heaviest demands are made on district nursing, physiotherapy, occupational therapy, chiropody and aids and appliances (including those for the incontinent). Moreover, with the ongoing application of the principle of continuing care in the community, which is, in the words of Victor, 'a hallmark of the approach and philosophy of geriatric medicine,'[22] the pressure on these services will intensify. In this context, it is worth noting that 'transfer' is a more appropriate term to use than 'discharge' for describing the movement of the elderly between hospitals and other institutions and the community.[23]

Last, in recent years there have been a number of studies which have suggested that women are more susceptible to ill health than men and demonstrated that women of all ages 'make greater use of health services than do men'.[24] For example, surveys have shown that 'rates of depression and/or anxiety for women are approximately twice those for men'.[25] Moreover, the rates are particularly high for women who are responsible for the care of young children, especially if they do not have paid employment. This is likely to be due to a combination of factors including the nature of the domestic role; social isolation; reduced income; unrealistic expectations which many women find it difficult to fulfil; and their greater willingness to seek help. Thus, as the authors of *Changing the Public Health* point out, 'many women's lives are especially stressful ... (and) the magnitude of the adversity (which they) face in their everyday lives (affects) ... their psychological well-being'.[26]

Although the determinants of health status are not fully understood, it is now generally accepted that gender plays a part, along with other social, cultural and physiological factors. Arguably, inequalities in health are related to the unequal control that exists over working and living conditions.[27] In general, women have less control than men.

If CHSs are to develop in an effective way, those responsible must take account of these factors. In view of the predominance of women as users this often involves paying particular attention to their distinctive needs. However, in so doing, it is important to avoid anything which reinforces existing gender roles and relationships and discourages men from taking advantage of the services available and from playing a full part in the maintenance of the health of households. Much of the evidence suggests that demographic, cultural and socio-economic change is resulting in a redefinition of the roles and responsibilities of men and women and of the nature and composition of households.[28]

Moreover, epidemiological trends may well lead to increasing contact between providers of community health care and those with whom they have previously had little contact (e.g. young men with AIDS).

From a practical point of view, these changes mean that CHSs staff should ensure that high priority is given to:

- gathering information about the socio-economic composition of the community served and the gender balance of the users of each service;
- identifying and avoiding stereotyping, with respect to gender, sexual orientation and type of household, in the planning and delivery of services;
- preparing training materials which foster sensitivity to gender issues on the part of those providing services;
- designing health promotion campaigns which acknowledge the changing roles and status of women and men;
- siting and the disposition of facilities in a way which maximises accessibility for all users, regardless of their gender and takes account of the fact that women are less likely to have access to private transport;
- fostering a psychological environment within which users feel comfortable and are not deterred; and
- monitoring the impact on women of changes in the level of funding and the organisation of services.[29]

In other words, in seeking to accommodate the 'personhood' and 'best interest' of clients in the planning and delivery of services, gender must be a major consideration. If the challenges arising from the 'crisis in health' (see Chapter 1) and the complexity of the values associated with community health care (see Chapter 2) are to be met, then the predominance of women in the CHSs has to be given full recognition and the needs of female employees, informal carers and users must be addressed more explicitly than has been the case in the past. The specific needs of women as workers, carers and users must be given equal priority with those of men. Only in this way can genuine equality of opportunity be secured.

Whether as providers or as users of CHSs, the role of women is constrained and coloured by their subordinate position in the wider society. It is the increasing interest in, and concern with, the place of women in society that provides the focus for the next section of this chapter.

Women in Society

Although disquiet concerning the status of women in society is by no means a new phenomenon, in recent years it has engendered many far-reaching changes. For example, legislative measures since the mid-1970s have removed some of the obstacles women face by making it illegal to discriminate on grounds of gender in areas such as employment and education. In addition, there have been cultural changes, brought about by attempts to detect and remove sexism, and thereby make attitudes and practices, in respect of women, less chauvinistic and more conducive to the pursuit of genuine equality of opportunity.

Clearly, the CHSs have not been immune from developments of this kind. Moreover, because of the large number of women within the CHSs, staff have an important part to play in promoting female interests. This means not only ensuring that measures of the kind outlined earlier in the chapter are implemented but also adopting a more proactive stance in respect of the rights of women. Indeed, more staff should become advocates for the cause of equality between the sexes and non-discriminatory health care services. Health visitors have taken the lead in this respect and have been prepared to articulate in the public arena their concerns regarding the unfair manner in which women are still treated and the way in which their 'personhood' and 'best interest' have been neglected.

Such an approach is vital. For, notwithstanding the very obvious legal changes which have taken place, there are many who dispute their efficacy and cast doubts on their real impact. They draw attention to the fact that women continue to occupy a lowly and marginal status in society with respect to income, wealth and occupation, and suggest that the changes do not represent a genuine challenge to the firmly established patterns of gender inequality. In support of this contention they point to the continuing dominance of men within the family; to the concentration of women in lower paid jobs; and to the problems faced by women who have secured professional status. Each of these aspects is now examined in a little more detail, with particular attention to their significance for the CHSs and to areas where those with responsibility for the delivery of services need to be sensitive to the importance of gender.

Within the **family**, traditionally the woman's domain, the claim that there is now greater equality between the sexes and more democratic gender relationships is not borne out in practice. Men are still regarded as the head of the household for the purposes of collecting many official statistics, paying bills and borrowing money, which clearly presents problems for women who are the head of a household. Very often men do not share domestic tasks equally with their partners, even in cases where the latter are also in paid employment. Time for leisure pursuits tends to be unfairly distributed and an alarming number of women and children are subject to violence within their homes.

Some of the more extreme consequences of this ongoing inequality are seen at first hand by CHSs staff. All too frequently they have to deal with the adverse effects on health of stress and anxiety amongst women; of the neglect and abuse of children; and of homelessness consequent upon women and children fleeing from violence. In responding to problems of this kind it is becoming increasingly clear that unless attention is given to their underlying cause, namely gender inequalities, there can be little hope of resolving them. Although there are, of course, no easy ways of securing a more equitable distribution of power between women and men within the family, CHSs staff are strategically placed to make a contribution in this respect. Through their contact with the victims of gender inequality they are likely to be more aware of the need to address the fundamental question of the unequal power of women and therefore to take positive action to secure its rightful place on the social policy agenda. Moreover, constant exposure to the extreme consequences of gender inequality should foster a more sensitive approach to the way in which the health needs of families are handled.

Clearly, not all women are directly at risk from male oppression. It is not inevitable that the unequal distribution of power will give rise to the situations outlined earlier. Indeed, when women and men live together harmoniously their relationship may be one of mutual support as far as their health needs are concerned and one which may afford protection 'against the negative effects of (stressful) life events', such as bereavement, moving house, career changes and childbirth.[30]

However, it would be both wrong and naive to conclude from this that, apart from taking steps to deal with the most urgent and obvious problems arising from gender inequality, nothing further needs to be done. From the available evidence it is clear that in family settings there are other, more subtle, threats to the health, 'best interest' and 'personhood' of women. For example, men expect, and receive, emotional support from the relationship but are not always prepared to reciprocate, which may partly explain the paradox of married women who describe themselves as lonely. Thus, even where the relationship is a loving one, there are likely to be more dividends for the male than for the female partner and their health status is not necessarily equal. This is particularly the case when women seek to take advantage of the expanded opportunities in the field of employment or, out of necessity, combine a domestic or informal caring role with that of paid employee. Typically, women who take up paid employment continue to shoulder the burden of managing the home and, more significantly, caring for children and other dependents. In other words, women are more likely than men to be faced with the dilemmas and stress involved in balancing the demands of informal caring with those of paid employment. Thus, given the importance of the contribution which women make to community health care, this should be a matter of particular concern to those responsible for the management and delivery of the services. Moreover, with the continued attention being given by academics, such as Hochschild, Oakley, Brannen and Moss,[31] to the dilemmas facing women who perform a dual role, CHSs staff are well placed to inform the debate and should not hesitate to do so.

Women's paid employment tends to be **concentrated in low paid, part-time, enabling jobs.**[32] This is due not only to practical considerations, such as their lack of formal qualifications, other demands on their time and the absence of support (e.g. publically funded childcare facilities)[33], but also to the processes of education and socialisation which prepare women for supportive and caring roles. In view of the very large numbers of women working in the CHSs it is not surprising that many of the jobs they perform, such as auxilliary nursing, selling welfare foods and acting as clinic clerks and receptionists, come into this category. Thus, it can be argued that CHSs managers should accept, at the very least, a moral responsibility for furthering the cause of equal pay and conditions of service and promoting the 'personhood' of women. Furthermore, with impending recruitment problems arising from the demographic 'time bomb' (see Chapter 1), there are pragmatic reasons for doing so. In other words, everything possible should be done to ensure that policy makers at all levels respond appropriately to the need for female and male employees to be treated equally. This is clearly more difficult to achieve in those areas of employment where there is gender segregation. Ironically, however, when job segregation is reduced by encouraging men to enter 'female' occupations this typically restricts the promotion opportunities of women.

In order to demonstrate their commitment to the cause of equal opportunities, CHSs managers should also set an example by taking steps to enhance the status of low paid, enabling jobs, for which they are directly responsible, and to increase the motivation of the job holders. This means giving due attention to the training and development needs of the staff concerned and to the application of techniques designed to increase their job interest, such as job rotation, job enlargement, job enrichment and the formation of autonomous work groups. In this way the content of jobs can be made more varied and rewarding and job holders can receive greater recognition for, and satisfaction from, the tasks they perform. In other words, 'personhood' should be respected in the design of jobs.

Unfortunately, initiatives of this kind are likely to have only a limited impact. This is because traditionally many of the tasks and activities associated with women have been undervalued and, in some cases, trivialised. Consequently, CHSs staff do not get the resources they need and informal care does not receive the wider recognition it deserves. One way of changing this situation is to continue to address the issue of 'equal pay for work of equal value' and to ensure that the 'best interest' of women is taken fully into account in the calculation of the greater good (see Chapter 2).

The undervaluation of 'women's work' is apparent not only in low paid jobs but also in the more prestigious, **professionally based jobs** which larger numbers of women are now able to secure as a result of legislative and cultural change. For example, physiotherapy, which is a typically female profession, lacks the kudos of a male dominated profession like medicine. This was demonstrated in the results of a survey carried out to ascertain 'the reason for the low proportion of men in physiotherapy'. Interestingly, but not surprisingly, the female image, lack of status, (relatively) poor salaries and low prestige were found to be the principal deterrents. In commenting on the survey, Davies claimed that: 'Men have as much to offer the profession as women', but he justified this in a rather provocative manner by highlighting gender related differences within the profession. He drew attention to what he perceived as the 'curing' and 'caring' aspects of physiotherapy and equated them with 'traditional male and female characteristics'.[34] In other words, in order to improve the status of the job it is necessary to stress those aspects which are considered to be typically masculine. Predictably, where men do enter professions of this kind, it becomes more difficult for women rise to the top. They may even find themselves marginalised where they continue to be associated with the female, caring aspects of the work. As Williams argues, 'gender inequalities, male domination and the sexual division of labour (are) often reproduced' in professional and occupational relationships.[35]

Even where women do hold senior posts in professions such as health visiting, district nursing, speech therapy and occupational therapy the disproportionate influence of men can still be felt in the determination of policies, priorities, working practices and personnel procedures. This can be illustrated by reference to the difficulties associated with the development of teamwork. Arguably one of the principal reasons why the concept of the primary health care team has failed to take root is the unwillingness of members of a male dominated branch of the medical profession (i.e. general practice) to collaborate on equal terms with members of female dominated branches of the nursing profession (i.e. health visiting and district nursing). Even where a willingness to cooperate does exist, attempts at securing effective teamworking are often blighted by gender relationships. For example, as Twomey points out: 'Developing good communications is clearly difficult if one member of the team sees himself as superior to or more important than the others'.[36] Undoubtedly, this has far-reaching implications for the future development of satisfactory community health care, which depends upon effective collaboration.

The concept of the primary care team is being undermined still further by trends in general practice which have gender connotations. Of particular significance is the employment by many GPs of a wider range of mainly female practice staff. Their increasing involvement in the provision of family planning services, screening, health promotion and other services is at the expense of professionals, such as health visitors, who have considerably more autonomy. Thus, any semblance of teamwork is in danger of being superseded by a hierarchical relationship in which female practitioners are controlled by predominantly male employers. Moreover, as Skinner has claimed, the absence of appropriate management arrangements and agreed training programmes for practice nurses has meant that some have been required by their GPs to carry out procedures which are beyond their competence. In so doing, they are in breach of the provisions of their professional code of conduct.[37] Clearly, this completely negates the principle of a team of professionals working together for the good of their clients.

Despite the best efforts of those who seek to foster teamwork (e.g. Cumberlege), productive collaboration will be achieved only if there is mutual respect and equality of status between members of different professions. This means, in effect, recognising the underlying and pervasive influence of gender and seeking to redress the balance of power between the sexes.

A key role in opening up for debate some of the issues raised in this section has been played by the feminist movement. Significantly, many of those who write from a feminist perspective have addressed aspects of health care and it is the desire to apply their insights to community based health care services which provides the third reason for highlighting the importance of gender issues in this book.

Feminism and Health

At the heart of the feminist critique of health care is the view that clinical practice and institutions are patriarchal.[38] Criticism is focused particularly on the medicalisation of the reproductive function of women; standard treatments (which tend to rely heavily on technology and intervention rather than prevention and self-care); and medical power relationships (which mirror gender relationships in the family). Many feminists go further and see clinicians as agents of social control.[39] They argue that control is secured through the definition of the cause and aetiology of disease; its diagnosis and its management; and the surveillance of mothering and sexuality. For example, it is the doctor who determines who is 'sick' and thus ascribes the status of 'patient' with the relief from responsibility and the access to treatment which this implies. Similarly, health visitors and school doctors and nurses help to define the 'proper' role of the mother.

Contrary to popular belief, these decisions are not objective ones based on incontrovertible scientific knowledge. They are influenced by the values, beliefs, and preconceptions of those making them and these, in turn, are the product of a particular socio-cultural system and ethical frame of reference (see Chapter 2), which feminists contend are patriarchal in their orientation. As a result, regardless of whether or not clinicians are male, women will be expected to be passive, to perform their 'proper' role as wives and mothers and to be able and willing to act as carers. In addition, they will be assumed to lack the capacity for rational self-determination and the right to make moral choices. On occasions these expectations can mean that certain women are denied access, not only to abortion, sterilisation and contraception, but also to therapies and caring services. Others are encouraged to accept medical interventions with which they are not entirely happy, for example the use of drugs in dealing with problems related to menstruation, the menopause and childbirth.

It is, of course, important to point out that there is rarely any conscious intent on the part of clinicians to engage in social control. Indeed, many would be deeply offended by the suggestion that they were doing anything other than applying their scientific knowledge and experience in an objective manner. According to feminists, however, patriachical attitudes and practices are so deeply embedded in contemporary culture that they are not recognised. Moreover, the biomedical approach to health care (see Chapter 1), which these attitudes and practices underpin, is assumed to be the only way of interpreting and responding to illness. In their view, the influence of this approach on health care is consummate and its impact on the health and well-being of women is far-reaching.

Disaffection from the dominant biomedical approach, with its alleged male bias, has led feminists to seek alternative perspectives on health and illness and new approaches to service delivery. At the forefront of the feminist challenge to conventional health care is the WHM which became a recognised force in the late 1960s.[40] It would like to shift the existing bureaucratic, professionalised and authoritarian system of health care, which reflects utilitarian values, in the direction of a service model based on feminist principles (i.e. shared knowledge and control; the flattening of hierarchies; a bias towards community based care; and the blurring of distinctions between professional service providers and clients). Such a model implies greater respect for the 'personhood' of carers and users, as well as providers.

This apparently coherent approach actually conceals a variety of different theoretical perspectives within the WHM. As a result, some commentators, such as Foster, have been critical of the movement with respect as much to its ideological heterogeneity, as to its lack of structure and the vagueness of its goals.[41]

Within the WHM there are broadly two opposing standpoints. One claims that 'compulsory familism' is built into the social fabric and that public provision for dependent people will never do more than 'top up' family based services extracted from women. Consequently, feminist health care can be provided only outside patriarchal institutions. In practice, this means establishing 'women only' self-help groups and clinics as a genuine alternative to those currently provided. Moreover, women are urged to withdraw their unpaid labour from males.

In contrast, there are those who promote what Williams describes as 'welfare feminism'.[42] They are keen to extend, rationalise and legitimise the roles and values of women, within existing structures, and to celebrate, rather than decry, women's traditional caring and nurturing functions. They seek to promote the preference of women for collectivism rather than individualism. Dalley, for example, argues for a significant expansion of community based health care services funded out of taxation in the interests of providing a liberating alternative to 'compulsory familism'.[43] This implies that an extension of the 'personhood' of women is in the 'best interest' of both sexes. Consequently, women and men should have comparable opportunities for paid employment and equal access to a range of high quality public services.

Given that the modern feminist movement has had a relatively short time in which to develop and refine theories to explain the position of women in society based on a systematic exploration of their experiences, such 'contradictions within feminist theory and practice' are not surprising. Moreover, many would argue that differences of view should not be allowed 'to fragment and divide' the WHM, but should be used in a constructive way to contribute to the growth of the movement and to the development of a genuinely feminist approach to health care.[44]

Indeed there is much common ground within the movement. Furthermore, there is considerable scope for mutual support and cooperation between feminists and those dedicated to the cause of community health care. This is because the functions, objectives and expertise of staff and the non-hospital settings within which services are delivered, make the community an appropriate setting, both in organisational and in cultural terms, for applying feminist principles to health care. In other words, feminists could do worse than look to the CHSs for opportunities to put their ideals into practice and to ensure that the autonomy, dignity and privacy of women are incorporated into the calculation of the greater good.

Equally, those with a commitment to community based health care can find intellectual support and theoretical vindication from the feminist movement. They can derive from this source greater legitimacy for many of the services, activities and approaches they wish to promote, even if their primary motivation is not essentially a feminist one.

In order to realise the potential benefits for both the WHM and the CHSs practical steps are being taken in a number of fields. These include: well-woman centres; self-help; information dissemination; and political action.

The development of **well-woman centres** began in Islington in the early 1970s. Since then they have been established in many parts of the country. According to a national guidelines document produced by Manchester CHCs in 1983, the principal aims and objectives of well-woman centres are to provide:

- a service specifically for women, which meets all their health care needs in a relaxed and friendly atmosphere;
- an accessible service available to all women; and
- a service run by women for women.[45]

However, as Thornley points out, in pursuing these aims and objectives three different 'models' have emerged. First, there are centres in which service providers adhere to the biomedical approach and offer a range of services and facilities 'based on the medical perceptions of health developed from ... cervical cytology clinics.' These include a full medical check up (e.g. weight and blood pressure recording, rubella screening, cervical smears); instruction on self-examination of the breasts; advice on family planning and psycho-sexual problems; and, if necessary, referral to appropriate agencies. Second, in some centres a 'holistic' approach to health care has been adopted. This is based on the belief that full account must be taken not only of a woman's physical needs but also of her social, emotional and psychological well-being. In centres of this kind particular attention is given to the need to 'demystify medicine' and to treat women 'as equal participants in their health care.' The third 'model' incorporates the 'self-help philosophy which encourages an awareness of how women may adopt a positive attitude to their health and lifestyles through mutual support'. Thus, emphasis is placed on informality; egalitarian structures; sharing experiences and knowledge; health education; and ensuring that women have both the understanding and confidence to make informed choices about their health.[46]

To some extent, all of these 'models' reflect a set of loosely linked feminist principles which are appropriate for community health care and which many CHSs staff already espouse. Of particular importance are the principles of equality of access and provision; active participation by clients in the caring process; treatment by non-invasive methods wherever possible; lay control; and self-help. By applying principles of this kind, not only in developing services specifically for women but also in other contexts, such as the care of the elderly, of people with disabilities and members of ethnic minority groups, CHSs staff can bring about valuable and fundamental changes in the way that service providers relate to clients and the environment within which many services are delivered.[47]

Arguably, of the principles mentioned earlier, it is that of **self-help** which has so far had the greatest impact beyond the confines of well woman centres. In recent years, there has been a proliferation of self-help groups concerned with typically female complaints, such as cystitis, post-natal depression, pre-menstrual tension and eating disorders. They are reminiscent of the consciousness-raising groups of the 1970s and can be regarded as a step in the direction of an alternative model of health care. Self-help enables members of the lay constituency to become active participants in the process of health maintenance rather than passive recipients or consumers of services delivered to them. They share information and draw upon their own implicit knowledge. Whereas this can be considered a positive development, it also reflects a high level of dissatisfaction amongst clients and some service providers with the conventional biomedical approach to many female complaints, which is based on stereotypes of women (e.g. the assumption that many disorders will be mitigated if women fulfil their reproductive function). Moreover, many treatments associated with the biomedical approach have often been inadequate and have been developed in ways which militate against the interests of women (e.g. drug therapies which give rise to dependency).

Thus, self-help groups serve as a vehicle for the application of feminist principles outside, if not entirely separate from, the formal health care system. The status of the client is enhanced and while the professional continues to have an important role, it is that of facilitator rather than that of direct provider. Treatments are non-invasive and the environment is more likely to be informal, friendly and supportive.

Some CHSs staff, in particular health visitors, have long subscribed to the view that self-help is a legitimate response to certain of the health needs of men as well as women. Thus, they have been instrumental in establishing support groups for those dependent on tranquillisers and on alcohol and for those with eating problems and in encouraging the spread of groups of this kind. In this way they can be said to have contributed to the 'diffusion of innovation' as far as self-help is concerned and they have set an example for other CHSs staff to follow.

Moreover, it is important for service providers and managers to recognise that, in view of the 'crisis in health', self-help has a further advantage over and above those arising from its appropriateness in meeting certain needs. From a financial point of view, it is a less costly form of care than that based on one-to-one encounters between clinicians and clients and is therefore attractive to budget holders. In other words, it is form of care which can represent good 'value for money'.

Another field in which there is scope for collaboration is that of **information dissemination**. Feminists and CHSs staff both recognise the importance of information as a resource and the power which it confers. This recognition is especially important with respect to the information needs of a culturally diverse population. Indeed, adequate information is essential if women are to pursue alternative forms of health care through well women centres and self-help groups. Publications ranging from books like the *Good Birth Guide* and *Our Bodies Ourselves*[48] to leaflets and videos on female physiology and every aspect of health care[49] all play a part in ensuring that people have access to relevant information, both clinical and organisational. More proactive forms of information dissemination include health exhibitions and fairs;[50] health promotion in schools and places of work; and parentcraft classes.

Clearly, there is much to be gained from sharing responsibility for the preparation and distribution of materials of this kind. First, the quality, both in terms of content and design, is likely to be enhanced if expertise is pooled. There is also a greater likelihood that the language used will be comprehensible to those for whom it is intended. Second, more people will be reached since feminists and CHSs staff have access to complementary networks. Third, scarce resources will be used more effectively. Because of its importance, not only in the context of gender, but also for the CHSs generally, the theme of information is discussed in greater detail in Chapter 4.

Common cause can also be made between feminists and CHSs staff in the field of **political action**. Regardless of the party in power nationally there will always be a need for action to ensure that the issues raised in this chapter receive the recognition they deserve from politicians and managers and thereby secure their rightful position on the political and health care agendas. Given the community of interest which exists between the WHM and many of the professional bodies acting on behalf of CHSs staff, there would seem to be considerable scope for coalition-building on the political front. For example, many within the WHM and the HVA share a concern for the health care problems of mothers on low incomes and a commitment to campaigning on their behalf. Similarly, feminists and CHSs staff have a common interest in articulating the needs of female informal carers and, in so doing, putting pressure on policy makers to provide adequate support for them.

Whatever strategies are adopted, it is essential that feminists and CHSs staff work together when their interests overlap. In spite of the divisions within the WHM, many feminists are working within the formal health care system in order to promote the 'best interest' of women. Equally, CHSs staff must not eschew political action, on the grounds that it is distasteful or irrevelant. As the authors of *Changing the Public Health* point out, 'health and disease **are** political issues, simply because they are profoundly influenced by political decisions and power relationships (emphasis added).' Indeed, 'controversial issues too often turn out to be those that threaten vested interests, one of the abilities of which is to define what shall be regarded as controversial.'[51] For example, the number of women addicted to prescription drugs has recently forced its way onto the political agenda, in spite of the drug companies' consummate skill in keeping the issue submerged for a long time. This demonstrates not only what can be achieved, but also what still needs to be done and the importance of constant vigilence if this kind of issue is to retain a relatively high profile.

Thus, a good case can be made for feminists and those concerned with the CHSs recognising and capitalising on their interdependence. They have many areas of common interest and, although their approach and political stance may be different, the benefits of collaboration far outweigh any disadvantages.

Gender issues must be addressed if community health care is to be equally available, culturally acceptable and physically accessible in accordance with the values on which the NHS was founded (see Chapter 2). As has been demonstrated, at least in numerical terms, women are disproportionately represented within the CHSs. A large majority of formal providers are female; there are more women than men engaged in the provision of informal care; and women are more likely than men to be either the direct or indirect users of services. However, despite attempts to improve the status of women in society, the ubiquity of women within the CHSs is not reflected in the prevailing value system, the decision making process and power structure. In calculating the greater good, women's interests still have a relatively low priority and there is a failure to acknowledge the equal right of women to be self-determining and to be accorded dignity. This is both unacceptable on moral grounds and misguided from a practical point of view.

In the light of points made in this chapter; the implications of various strands of the 'crisis in health'; and the value framework presented in Chapter 2, there is clearly a very strong case for striving to ensure that women's needs as providers, carers and users determine the style and pattern of health care provided in community settings. Moreover, services will be more effective and better use will be made of scarce resources if due consideration is given to the distinctive needs, preferences and aspirations of female employees, informal carers and users.

It is upon women that the CHSs have always relied and to whom they have been primarily directed. Their future well-being depends upon full recognition being given to the centrality of women in community health care and to the application of female insights in the planning and delivery of services.

Notes

1 For example, St Georges Hospital Medical School, Tooting, conceded, in 1988, that its admission procedures discriminated against female applicants.

2 F. Williams, *Social Policy: A Critical Introduction* (Oxford: Polity Press, 1989) p.76. For further discussion of this issue see:

J. Dale and P. Foster, *Feminists and State Welfare* (London: Routledge and Kegan Paul, 1986);
G. Pascall, *Social Policy: A Feminist Analysis* (London: Tavistock Publications, 1986);
S. V. Rosser (ed.), *Feminism within the Science and Health Care Professions: Overcoming Resistance* (Oxford: Pergamon Press, 1988);
M. Stacey, *The Sociology of Health and Healing* (London: Unwin Hyman, 1988); and
H. Pizurki, A. Mejia, I. Butter and L. Ewart, *Women as Providers of Health Care* (Geneva: WHO, 1987).

3 For example, over ninety percent of registered physiotherapists, speech therapists and occupational therapists are women.

4 In 1991, a health authority was so concerned about staff shortages that it asked the EOC to help it prepare for the projected shortfall caused by a twenty five percent drop in the number of school leavers.

5 EOC, *Equality Management:Women's Employment in the NHS*, 1991, para.5.

6 The EOC has recommended that, at local level, health authorities, units and trusts should:

'establish equal opportunities policies and practices, eliminate sex and marital discrimination in recruitment and employment policies, and introduce family friendly policies ...
adopt written equal opportunities policies ...
review all policies to ensure that they cover sex and marital discrimination ..
establish equal opportunities committees in order to implement policy and facilitate change ...
formulate action plans to set out the priorities for the implementation of equal opportunities policies ...
introduce monitoring systems to identify possible discrimination ...
use positive action sections of the sex ... discrimination legislation to redress areas of past discrimination ...
ensure the elimination of discrimination ...
extend training in recruitment and selection ...
provide written equal opportunities guidelines for all managers ... remove all discriminatory questions from application forms ...
ensure equal pay and lawful payment structures ...
consider the provision and adequacy of childcare arrangements ...'

In addition, RHAs should 'set detailed equality targets as part of the equality review process' and 'ensure that such targets are included in trust applications.' See also the report from the All Wales Management Efficiency Group, *Manpower resources and the future: the need for flexibility and innovation*, 1991; S Corby, 'When two halves make total sense', *The Health Service Journal*, 18 July 1991, pp.20-2; and J. Naish, 'Women's work and working women: childcare and the NHS', Health Visitor, vol.63, no.3, March 1990, pp.85-6.

7 See, for example, M. Dutson and A, O'Neil, 'Job Sharing', *Journal of District Nursing*, February 1990, p.19, and New Ways to Work, *Job Sharing in the Health Service*, February 1989.

8 See, for example, C. Hancock, 'Bringing Nursing under Control', *THS Health Summary*, October 1991.

9 Informal care has been the subject of considerable interest and debate in the academic world, especially since the early 1980s. See, for example, A. Walker, *Community Care: The Family, State and Social Policy* (Oxford: Basil Blackwell and Martin Robertson, 1982) and C. Victor, *Health and Health Care in Later Life* (Milton Keynes: Open University Press, 1991), esp. pp.149-155.

10 H. Green, *Informal Carers: A study carried out on behalf of the Department of Health and Social Security as part of the 1985 General Household Survey* (London: HMSO, 1988). For this study 'carers' were defined as 'people who were looking after or providing some regular service for a sick, handicapped or elderly person living on their own or in another household'. Interestingly, this definition excludes those caring for children, whereas 'in the countries of Scandinavia, no distinction is made between 'caring' for dependent people who are not children and caring for children'. For further details, see C. Ungerson (ed.), *Gender and Caring: Work and Welfare in Britain and Scandinavia* (London: Harvester Wheatsheaf, 1990). Because of the distinction made in this country it has been decided to leave discussion of the contribution of women to the health of children until later in the chapter.

11 DH, *Caring for People - Community Care in the Next Decade and Beyond*, CM 849, (London: HMSO, 1989), para.1.11.

12 For a more detailed discussion of this point, see J. Brotchie and D. Hills, *Equal Shares in Caring: Towards Equality in Health* (London: Socialist Health Association, 1991).

13 F. Badger, E. Cameron, H. Evers and R. Griffiths, 'Facing Care's Unequal Shares', *The Health Service Journal*, 24 November 1988, pp.1392-3. See also, S. Arber, 'Revealing women's health: re-analysing the General Household Survey' in H. Roberts (ed.), *Women's Health Counts* (London: Routledge, 1990).

14 For a full discussion of the guilt, divided loyalties and other emotions experienced by women seeking to combine two roles, see A. Myrdal and V.

Klein, *Women's Two Roles: Home and Work* (London: Routledge and Kegan Paul, 1968) and J. Brannen and P. Moss, *Managing Mothers: Dual Earner Households after Maternity Leave* (London: Unwin Hyman, 1990).

15 This plan forms part of the New Deal for Carers campaign, which was launched in 1989 by a variety of organisations including the Carers National Association, Kings Fund, National Schizophrenia Fellowship, Alzheimers Disease Society and Age Concern. For further details, see *Carelink*, no.7, Spring 1989.

16 F. Badger et.al., op.cit. This view, however, is challenged by other commentators, who argue that women are likely to continue to take on the double burden of care and paid jobs. See, for example, J. Finch, *Who's Responsibility? Women and the Future of Family Care, Informal Care Tomorrow*, Occasional Paper, Policy Studies Institute, 1987. Nevertheless, whatever happens, CHSs managers will still be faced with major challenges in seeking to implement the principles of care in the community.

17 It is noteworthy that the clients using these services are not truly representative of women. For example, lesbians and post-menopausal women are less likely to make use of them than others.

18 H. Graham, *Women, Health and the Family* (Brighton: Wheatsheaf Books Ltd, 1985), p.70.

19 For further discussion of the mediating role of women, see F. Williams, op.cit., p.183.

20 For further details, see B. Mayall and M-C. Foster, *Child Health Care. Living with Children, Working for Children* (Oxford: Heinemann Nursing, 1989) and H. Pizurki, A. Mejia, I. Butter and L. Ewart, op.cit.

21 For a discussion of the role of women in highlighting environmental conditions which are damaging to health, see B. Vallely, 'Women, health and the environment', *Health Visitor*, vol.64, no.2, February 1991, pp.44-6.

22 C. Victor, op.cit., p.119.

23 Ibid.

24. I. Reid and E. Stratta, *Sex Differences in Britain* (Aldershot: Gower, 1989), p.55.

25 L. Smith, 'Women and Mental Health' in J. Orr (ed.), *Women's Health in the Community* (Chichester: Wiley, 1987), p.76.

26 Research Unit in Health and Behavioural Change, *Changing the Public Health* (Chicester: Wiley, 1989), p.110. There is, however, evidence to suggest that considerable variations exist amongst women. For example, the incidence of diagnosed schizophrenia is much higher amongst females born in the UK with an Afro-Caribbean background, than amongst white women. While there is a lower incidence of depression amongst Asian women. Nevertheless, this diversity may well reflect the expectations and predispositions of medical practitioners rather than real differences in the

level of illness. For further details, see R. Littlewood and M. Lipsedge, 'Psychiatric illness among British Afro-Carribbeans', *British Medical Journal*, vol.296, 2 April 1988, pp.950-1. Whatever the reality of the situation, it is significant that, according to Malcolm Lader, Professor of Clinical Psychopharmacology at the Institute of Psychiatry, two-thirds of those addicted to prescribed tranquillisers are women.

27 See M.G. Marmot, 'Social Inequalities in Mortality: the social environment' in R.G. Wilkinson (ed.), *Class and Health: research and longitudinal data* (London: Tavistock, 1986).

28 Note, for example, that in 1988 one in six of all families with dependent children was headed by a single parent and that only one in ten of these was a man. For further details, see *Population Trends 65* (London: HMSO, Autumn 1991).

29 This is particularly important since there is evidence to suggest that women are being disproportionately disadvantaged by financial cutbacks and organisational change. See, for example, H. Harman and J. Richardson, *Health care for women, the impact of the NHS white paper* (London: Labour Party, 1989) and R. Newbigging, *Suffering the cuts: a survey of cuts in health services for women in London* (London: London Health Emergency, 1990).

30 A. Smith and B. Jacobson (eds.), *The Nation's Health : A Strategy for the 1990s* (London: Health Education Authority, London School of Hygiene and Tropical Medicine and King Edward's Hospital Fund for London, 1988), pp.135-6.

31 A. Hochschild with A. Machung, *The Second Shift* (London: Piatkus Books, 1990); A. Oakley, *Subject Women* (London: Fontana, 1982); and J. Brannen and P. Moss, op.cit.

32 For example, in the EOC Report, op.cit., the point is made that within the NHS women are overrepresented in those occupational groups which have the highest percentage of part-time workers, such as ancillary staff (55%) and nursing and midwifery (35% approx).

33 Britain's performance in this respect is very much worse than that of some other European countries. For example, figures produced by the Child Poverty Action Group show that in 1988 there were places in publicly funded nurseries for only 2% of British children aged under 3. At the same time, there were places for 20% of French children, 20% of Belgian children and, in 1989, for 48% of Danish children. For further details, see Child Poverty Action Group, *Europe: A Fairer Future*, 1989, p.10, and S. Finch and D. Morgan, *A Practical Guide to Partnership in Childcare* (London: Working for Childcare, 1992).

34 J. Davies, 'Physiotherapy: Where are the men?', *Physiotherapy*, vol.76, no.3, March 1990, pp.132-4.

35 F. Williams, op.cit., p.181.

36 M. Twomey, 'A Feminist Perspective in District Nursing' in C. Webb, *Feminist Practice in Women's Health Care* (Chichester: Wiley, 1986), p.53.

37 See J. Skinner, 'Practice Nursing: a growing concern' in S. Pike and E. O'Keefe (eds.), *Comments on Community Nursing to the Tomlinson Enquiry on the Future of London Health Services*, The School of Health Studies, The Polytechnic of North London, 1992.

38 For example, in discussing the education of health visitors, J. Orr, 'Feminism and Health Visiting' in C. Webb (ed.) *Feminist Practice in Women's Health Care* (London: Wiley and Sons, 1986), makes the point that even this reflects masculine values, since it is grounded in the experiences, perceptions and beliefs of men.

39 See, for example, B. Mayell and M-C. Foster, op.cit., where the social control inherent in a health vistor's role is discussed.

40 M. K. Zimmerman, 'The Women's Health Movement: A Critique of Medical Enterprise and The Position of Women' in B. B. Hess and M. M. Ferree (eds.), *Analysing Gender: A Handbook of Social Science Research* (Newbury Park, California: Sage Publications, 1987).

41 P. Foster, 'Improving the Doctor/Patient Relationship: A Feminist Perspective', *Journal of Social Policy*, vol.18, pt.3, July 1989, pp.337-361.

42 F. Williams, op.cit., pp.49-52.

43 G. Dalley, *Ideologies of Caring: rethinking community and collectivism* (Basingstoke: Macmillan Educational, 1988).

44 M. Zalewski, 'Logical Contradictions in Feminist Health Care: A Rejoinder to Peggy Foster', *Journal of Social Policy*, vol.19, pt.2, April 1990, pp.235-244.

45 Manchester's Community Health Councils, *National Guidelines for Well-Women Centres* (Manchester: Manchester's Community Health Councils, 1983).

46 P. Thornley, 'The Development of Well Woman Clinics' in J. Orr (ed.), op.cit., pp.97-106.

47 C. Pharoah and E. Redmond, 'Care for ethnic elders', *The Health Service Journal*, 16 May 1991, pp.20-1, give an example of what can be done in this respect, through the creation of a special health centre for elderly Asian women.

48 S. Kitzinger, *Good Birth Guide* (London: Penguin, 1983) and Boston Women's Health Collective, *Our Bodies Ourselves* (New York: Simon Schuster, 1976; London: Allen Lane and Pengiun, 1978). See also *Women Assertiveness and Health* (London: Health Education Authority, 1990) and M. Stewart with S. Tooley, *Beat PMT Cookbook* (London: Women's Nutritional Advisory Service, 1990).

49 Examples of booklets and leaflets include:

Cervical Cancer: It Can be Avoided. produced by Durex Contraception Information Service in cooperation with the Women's National Cancer Control Campaign.
Your Health: A Guide to Services for Women (London: Department of Health, 1991).
It is dangerous, however, to assume that these are necessarily of benefit to women. The DH booklet, for example, has been criticised by the Health Visitors' Association on the grounds that it is medically oriented, patronising, confusing and more likely to frighten than inform.

50 A good illustration of what is meant by the term 'women's health fair' and the potential for collaboration inherent in this kind of initiative is provided by an event held at Plymouth College of Further Education in April 1990. Although this was the fourth health fair to be staged in the South West, it was the first at which a wide range of organisations were represented (e.g. the health authority, family practitioner committee, community health council and voluntary bodies) and at which seminars were held. Topics discussed at seminars and workshops and on which information was available from stands included stress, the menopause, pre-menstrual tension, environmental health concerns and homeopathy. Other examples of what can be done in this respect include the Sheffield women's health bus and the women's health week held in the Toxteth area of Liverpool.

51 Research Unit in Health and Behavioural Change, op.cit., p.160.

CHAPTER 4

Information

Information is difficult to conceptualise because of its links with knowledge. In the sphere of health policy and in management literature the term tends to be used to refer to knowledge which is explicit and therefore relatively easy to record, classify and quantify. This would include not only readily observable phenomena, such as attendance rates at pre-school clinics, but also areas where judgement is involved, such as the identification and assessment of disability. In other words, information is often equated with knowledge which has been formalised and can be used for the purposes of comparison. It provides a language for planners, service providers and citizens to discuss health needs and policies. As indicated in Chapter 2, this is compatible with the utilitarian emphasis on observation and recording.

For the kantian, however, formal information provides only a partial picture, since it fails to take account of the meanings which individuals and communities attach, and the implicit knowledge which they bring, to their actions. At the heart of implicit knowledge are the assumptions, beliefs, attitudes and value judgements underlying behaviour, which are acquired through socialisation and that part of formal education often referred to as the hidden curriculum. Examples include: parents' reasons for attending pre-school clinics; the philosophy underpinning multicultural rehabilitation initiatives for older people;[1] mothers' intuitive understanding of whether their children are thriving; and the experiences of people with disabilities.[2] Unfortunately there is a tendency for planners and policy makers, in particular, to overlook implicit knowledge. This is because of its intangible, qualitative nature, which makes it difficult to record and creates a sense of unease. In practice, however, informal information of this kind plays as important a part in health care as formal information. For example, case notes will often include informal information about the client's state of mind, as well as formal information about drug regimes. Moreover, there is a burgeoning literature attesting to the recognition now being given to the impact on health of the different meanings that lay people and professionals bring to clinical encounters.[3] Thus, in this chapter, the term information will be used in its broader sense to refer to that derived from implicit as well as explicit knowledge.

For all aspects of community health care and all the constituencies involved, information is a key resource. 'It is essential in enabling clinical care of individual patients, it is the basis of both operational and strategic management, and it underlies the measurement and monitoring of public health.'[4] Moreover, it is of crucial importance for members of the lay constituency, since it enables them to make more effective use of health care services and to enhance their understanding of the wider environment within which health choices are made. Given the centrality of information as a resource it is one to which particular attention needs to be given.

To this end, an important first step is to identify the principal characteristics of information both as an organisational and as a personal resource, regardless of whether it has been derived from explicit or implicit knowledge. First, information has been subject to a number of processes, indeed if this were not the case it would be unusable. Some professionals, such as computer scientists and accountants, draw a clear distinction between information and data (from which it is constructed). Chandor, for example, states that 'information is derived from the assembly, analysis, or summarising of data into a meaningful form.'[5] However, it is wrong to assume from this that data are unprocessed. They are themselves 'produced' using classification schema (such as those relating to occupation, ethnicity, diagnostic category) and methods designed to help voluntary sector workers and lay people document their implicit knowledge. A second characteristic of information is that it incurs costs. Financial and other resources have to be expended to produce, store and use information. Despite the apparently obvious nature of this point it is one that can be easily lost sight of on a day to day basis. Third, information is potentially limitless. Therefore selection is central to its production, with all the difficulties of avoiding distortion that this implies. Fourth, information is a political resource in the sense that it confers power on those who possess it. Consequently, it can be the cause of conflicts across departmental, professional and organisational boundaries; between service providers and individual clients and client groups; and amongst differently placed groups within the population at large. Last, because information is seldom morally neutral, the processing of data and interpretation of information involve judgements which depend upon the perspectives and objectives of those involved and reflect their values and beliefs.

Another step is to recognise that information can be either 'good' or 'bad'. In the interests of promoting more effective decision making on the part of managers, service providers and service users, many commentators have addressed the question of what constitutes 'good' information. They have suggested that its most important qualities are:

- relevance to the activities and decisions concerned;
- the appropriateness of the mode and style of presentation;
- timeliness;
- accuracy;
- conciseness; and
- flexibility (i.e. wherever possible, it should be useable in a number of different contexts).

However, because of the large numbers of potential end-users of information there might well be conflicts of interest.

Although such considerations have always been important, in recent years they have been thrown into sharper relief by the development of microcomputing. This has revolutionised the processing of data and the production of information and has raised 'the expectations of both managers and professionals',[6] as well as service users and the public at large. It has also meant that managers and service providers are having to acquire new skills to enable them to cope with the information explosion and what has been termed the 'democratisation of information'.

With respect to the 'crisis in health', an important consequence of the greater availability of information is that it is far more difficult to ignore the very real problems and dilemmas inherent in health care (see Chapter 1). Furthermore, the position taken in respect of different aspects of the 'crisis' by those responsible for the CHSs, such as inequalities in health; the 'iceberg' of sickness and disability; consumerism; and the tension between needs and resources, will affect decisions relating to the production and use of information.

Since the early 1980s the growing importance of information on the health care agenda can be illustrated by reference to a number of initiatives. The most important of these are:

- the recommendations of the Working Party, chaired by Edith Korner, which examined the information requirements of health authorities during the first half of the 1980s;
- the development of performance and service indicators, which involve the quantification of various aspects of service planning and delivery so that 'the overall achievement level of an individual authority, unit, or other functional sub-division ... (can) be cast in a comparative perspective';[7]
- information strategies, whereby managers adopt a longer-term and more systematic approach to the identification and meeting of their information needs;
- resource management, designed to ensure that 'clinicians and other managers make better informed judgements about how the resources they control can be used to maximum effect';[8]
- the requirement that district health authorities (DHAs), in collaboration with family health services authorities (FHSAs) and other agencies, should systematically assess the health care needs of their populations (see Chapter 5);[9] and
- the publication of *The Health of the Nation. A Consultative Document for Health in England*, which highlights the importance of certain kinds of information in the setting and pursuit of health targets.[10]

In every case their impact has been felt in the CHSs.[11]

In looking at information from the perspective of community health care a number of underlying themes emerge. The first is that a far higher priority should be given to the development of information systems, and to the utilisation of information, within the CHSs. Despite recent initiatives community health information systems remain relatively underdeveloped. For example, in the case of the CHSs it has been argued that the 'Korner minimum data set (is) insufficient for addressing local management issues such as the deployment of resources ... and the planning of future services'.[12] Similarly, the resource management initiative has underestimated the difficulties surrounding the generation and integration of financial and non-financial information about community based clinical encounters and outcomes.

A second theme arises from the increasing concern for efficiency and 'value for money' within the NHS and the need for quantitative information (i.e. that derived from explicit knowledge) against which to measure progress Even though this is not necessarily wrong, caution should be exercised, particularly within the CHSs, because of the attendant danger that less easily quantifiable information (i.e. that derived from implicit knowledge) will be neglected. Therefore, although: 'Measuring health care in its broadest sense is difficult and measuring preventive and community health services more so',[13] every effort should be made to paint a full picture.

A third and final theme is that there should be a wholehearted commitment within the CHSs to greater openness and the sharing of information. This is because those responsible for the provision of services of this kind have far more to gain from the wider availability of good quality information than have their colleagues in other parts of the health care system. Arguably, the full potential of their preventive and caring roles can only be realised if comprehensive information is freely available to all interested parties, including clients and the public at large. Furthermore, the dearth of appropriate information about the need for services, such as that relating to morbidity and disability at local level, makes it easier to continue the underfunding of community based health care services. Moreover, information about needs and outcomes in community settings are a necessary condition even for simply maintaining the existing level of funding. Thus, CHSs staff should be at the forefront of the movement to secure greater freedom of information.

It is with these themes in mind that consideration is now given to some of the key issues associated with:

- the need for and the purpose of information within community health care, with particular attention being given to the information needs which arise from the proactive nature of various aspects of community based health care, service planning and delivery and the importance of involving members of the lay constituency in the health care process;
- the generation of data, including the design and operation of systems for capturing data and the costs involved;
- the conversion of data into information, that is the production and presentation of information in terms of its salience, accuracy, timeliness, volume, accessibility and dissemination;
- the links between information, attitudes, beliefs and behaviour; and
- the ownership of information.

Each of these issues provides a focus for the sections which follow.

The Need for and Purpose of Information within Community Health Care

Information is expensive. It is therefore essential to ensure that any decision to produce information can be justified in terms of the contribution which it will make to the quality of services and improvements in the health status of the population at large. In other words, there should be a clear and demonstrable need for the information and its primary purpose must be to facilitate the planning and delivery of effective community health care.

In reality, however, many other factors affect decisions relating to the production of information. First, custom and practice can play a part. For example, data are often collected on the grounds that they always have been, even though the original justification for collection is no longer valid and no use is made of it.[14] Second, some information is produced simply because it is relatively easy to do so. In the words of McArthur and Stone: 'Information has had a chequered history in the NHS because collection has always come before use'.[15] This is not only wasteful but may, in certain situations, divert attention from information which is more difficult to generate but would be of far greater value (e.g. patterns of chronic disease, peer group assessment and the views of clients with regard to health visiting and school nursing)[16]. Last, much of the information produced at local level is in response to requests from the centre. Although these may be legitimate in the sense that they originate from a desire to improve the quality of services, they may not be perceived as such by those directly engaged in the delivery and receipt of care. For this and other reasons the information collected is not always used to good effect. As Powell and Prothero point out, there is a constant danger that information will be 'collected solely to facilitate the completion of a central requirement ... rather than to provide information that is of use locally.'[17]

Whereas it is not possible to avoid these dangers completely, their effect can be minimised by constantly examining in a constructive, but critical, way the need for and purposes of information. In so doing, it is important for CHSs managers to recognise that each of the constituencies identified in Chapter 2 have somewhat different perspectives on information. Therefore they should not think that they have the sole or primary brief for taking decisions in this field.

To a great extent, the need for information on the part of those responsible for managing and delivering the CHSs arises from the proactive and caring nature of these services; their emerging role in the provision of complex treatment (e.g. that provided by diabetic liaison nurses and community psychiatric nurses); and the desire to ensure that resources are being used as efficiently and effectively as possible.

A number of specific information requirements can be identified within the CHSs.

- Demographic and epidemiological information of various kinds is needed to monitor general trends in mortality, morbidity and disability; to identify inequalities in health status, for planning purposes;[18] and to assess progress towards the achievement of specific health targets.[19] A key source of national, regional and district level information is the OPCS.[20] At sub-district level, many authorities are developing databases containing information about morbidity with respect to chronic illnesses (e.g. diabetes) and the geographic distribution of population groups (e.g. the elderly) and these are being used 'to plan healthcare throughout the district'.[21]
- Personal information is needed (e.g. name, age, gender, address, ethnic origin, health and socio-economic status) to locate members of defined groups for illness prevention purposes, such as screening, vaccination and immunisation.
- Access to quantitative and qualitative research findings concerning the links between health and lifestyle and environment (e.g. diet, occupation, housing conditions, leisure pursuits, alcohol) is needed to foster and develop the health maintenance role and to highlight conditions where collective action is required. This could be facilitated by the establishment of local research databases and wider use of unpublished studies such as projects undertaken by students and voluntary organisations.
- Regular audits of services provided by other agencies (e.g. family practitioners, voluntary organisations, local personal social services authorities, private sector organisations) should be undertaken to identify overlaps and gaps in their availability.
- The views and perceptions of clients, informal carers and the public at large should be canvassed and the use of existing services reviewed (e.g. by conducting surveys, establishing consultative machinery) to ensure that they are effective and reflect the wishes and preferences of those who use them.

- Educational materials are needed (e.g. advertisements, user guides and directories, health manuals) to enable clients to take more responsibility for their own health.
- Health professionals need to be better informed about the full range of community services if they are to respond positively to the findings of consumer surveys which invariably show that 'the public wants more information from professionals about health services'.[22]
- Staffing, budgetary and patient activity information is needed (e.g. the unit costs of home visits, the deployment of clinical staff) to manage resources efficiently and to monitor contractual performance.
- Information about the outcomes of different kinds of treatment and care is needed to facilitate the conduct of clinical audits.[23]
- It is necessary to learn from what is happening elsewhere by making use of bibliographic sources of information (e.g. books, journal articles, conference papers, reports) in order to develop new approaches to the management and delivery of services.

This is undoubtedly a formidable list and it is by no means comprehensive. Moreover, it does not fully reflect the need for information as perceived by service users. Nevertheless, it does provide a framework within which to assess the nature, and validity, of decisions to produce information.

Up till now there has been an assumption that it is relatively easy to reach general agreement with respect to the assessment of the need for information and the acceptability of producing certain kinds of information. This, however, is not the case, since information is a value laden resource. In practice, the question of who defines the need is a crucial one. Furthermore, ethical issues are involved, with each constituency viewing the relationship between values and knowledge in a different way.

The definition of need will be affected by the background, perspective, objectives, power and authority of those making the decision and the constraints upon them. For example, the managerial constituency is likely to be more constrained by resource considerations than the clinical constituency. Moreover, with regard to the production of information, central government has the authority to impose its will on those at the point of service delivery. Similarly, those who subscribe to the biomedical approach to health will have a different perspective on the need for information from those who think that social factors should also be taken into account.

Ethical considerations also arise from the personal nature of much of the data needed to produce good quality information. Some, for example, would question the rectitude of producing information about those who are apparently in good health and the invasion of privacy and the demands on time and energy which this involves. Even where the production of information commands widespread agreement a number of people would continue to defend, on kantian grounds, the individual's right not to be troubled in this way. Such considerations apply to an even greater extent in cases where there is a reluctance to provide information because it may be used to buttress discriminatory practices and to label people in situations where either stigma or illegality is involved (e.g. HIV infection, heroin use).

As argued in Chapter 2, such value laden questions need to be tackled in a deliberate manner and the decision making process opened up to the weaker constituencies. Once decisions have been made the next logical step is to consider the way in which the necessary data are to be acquired.

The Acquisition of Data

Many of the issues associated with the acquisition of data tend to be of a logistic nature. They arise from the complexities and costs involved in designing systems for the collection or capture of data, which are 'user friendly' and cost-effective. Furthermore, these considerations apply as much to the acquisition of bibliographic, documentary and organisational data as they do to those of a personal kind.

In the case of community based health care, some of the issues are compounded by the fact that services are dispersed and provided by a variety of agencies. As McArthur and Stone argue: 'It is far easier to monitor services provided in a hospital by a limited range of professionals working for the same authority, than to know what is being provided to people in their own homes (and elsewhere in the community).'[24] This makes it all the more important for CHSs staff to apply good practice when designing systems for acquiring data.

Clearly, one of the best ways of ensuring that systems are 'user friendly' is to involve the data capturers in their design. This is not necessarily as straightforward as it might seem. It is not always entirely clear who will be responsible for the capture of the data and how this responsibility might be shared between service providers, managers and members of the lay constituency. It is also difficult to find effective ways of securing their input to the design process.

Nevertheless, it is worth expending time and energy on the resolution of these problems and the establishment of good practice, since, as a number of commentators have argued, there are many advantages to be derived from end-user participation in determining the arrangements for the capture of data. These include generating interest, reducing anxiety, increasing confidence and minimising the alienation which results from the imposition of systems.[25] By involving lay people, as well as the other major constituencies, a working consensus can emerge within which participants can claim ownership of the processes for capturing data.

Moreover, where there is this ownership, systems are likely to be better designed. This means avoiding common weaknesses highlighted in the following critique of a community based system for the capture of personal data:

> *Many of the forms were badly designed, some of the data were not used at all, and data collection was often repeated by different people. This lead to a number of unnecessary errors and took up valuable client care time. The collection systems seemed to impede good relations between professionals and clients during consultations.*[26]

Thus, priority must be given to the effective design of forms and questionnaires and, where information technology (IT) is involved, making informed and acceptable choices between alternative data collection and entry devices (e.g. optical mark reader cards, portable and hand-held microcomputers, smart cards, VDUs). In so doing it is important to ensure that, in view of the costs involved, the data collected will be used and errors and duplication minimised. Steps must also be taken to avoid damaging the relationship between data capturers and clients, which might be at risk if the methods used are obtrusive or threatening and the client is not fully convinced of the purpose and value of the exercise.

Although particular attention has been given to the acquisition of personal data, it is important to recognise that these issues are equally relevant when considering the capture of other forms of data. For example, in seeking to gather data about the scale and quality of services provided by a voluntary organisation, a community unit/trust might inadvertantly undermine a good working relationship. Similarly CHSs staff need to foster interactive links with departments of public health which are sufficiently robust to ensure shared access to epidemiological data.

Whatever the nature of the data being captured, unless a high priority is given to the education and training of those involved, even the most 'user friendly' system is unlikely to be completely successful. The importance of training has been recognised by many community units/trusts. For example, in Croydon Community Unit's application for trust status reference was made to the fact that: 'Training ... in the collection ... of information has been a key developmental area in the past and will continue to be so.'[27] In this context, education and training should cover not only the technical aspects of data capture (e.g. how to operate a hand-held microcomputer; how to extract data from research reports) but also its human aspects, which includes respect for the 'personhood' of those involved (e.g. how to balance the demands of data capture with those of service provision; how to cope with the anxieties and fears of those to whom the data relate). In addition to the content of training programmes, a number of other issues are likely to arise. These include the relative contributions of in-house and college based courses; the most appropriate format for training of this kind; the roles of different types of trainer; and the funding implications.

Clearly cost considerations apply as much to other aspects of data capture as they do to education and training. There are not only direct costs arising from the purchase of equipment; the employment of staff; and the design, piloting and operation of systems; but also opportunity costs. In other words, the acquisition of data is inevitably at the expense of other activities, both clinical and managerial. It must therefore be justified in terms of the potential benefits to which it gives rise.

Difficulties arise, however, because those upon whom the costs fall may not always be the beneficiaries. Undoubtedly the worst scenario in this respect is one where clinicians bear the full brunt of the costs and the managers derive all or most of the benefits. Thus, every analysis of the costs and benefits of data capture should include an assessment not only of their magnitude but also of their incidence. In other words, it is important to determine, who benefits? If this is done, it is more likely that steps will be taken to ensure that those directly involved in the capture of data receive some benefit. This might take the form of a rationalisation of existing procedures for capturing data or improvements in the quality of the information available to front line staff.

In designing any system for capturing data, the aim must be to maximise benefits and minimise costs. This encompasses the tension-laden moral objective of securing the 'greatest good of the greatest number', while acknowledging the 'personhood' of individuals. The realisation of this objective depends primarily upon the availability of opportunities for members of all the constituencies to participate at every stage of the design process; to receive adequate education and training in all aspects of the system; and to test the system rigorously before it becomes fully operational. It is also necessary to make certain that the data captured are accurate and in a form which will allow them to be converted into information for which there is an established need. If this is not the case then clearly even the most cost-effective system of data capture will represent a waste of resources. Moreover, it has to be recognised that the establishment of systems takes a great deal of time, if it is to be done properly. There is a real danger that changes and developments will be rushed through with unseemly haste, thereby prejudicing their usefulness.

The Conversion of Data into Information

There is a temptation to regard the process by which data are converted into information as a purely technical matter and therefore one which can be left entirely to the experts. This has been reinforced by the fact that IT is now being used extensively for the purposes of data conversion. As Lattimer and Mason point out, 'some information such as routine patient costs can only be produced by installing sophisticated computer systems.'[28] Moreover, for the CHSs many recent developments, including the establishment and operation of effective health screening programmes, community profiling and targeting need, require the application of IT.

However, the temptation to allow the specialists a free hand must be resisted if the potential of the information is to be fully realised. Even though specialists in different aspects of data conversion and information presentation, such as systems analysts, statisticians and graphic designers, clearly have an important part to play, so also do those for whom the information is intended, that is the end-users. Again it must be emphasised that with respect to community health care these include not only managers and service providers but also clients, informal carers, voluntary organisations and the public at large.

The quality of information will be enhanced if end-users participate in making decisions about:

- the speed of the conversion process and the technology involved;
- the manner in which the information is structured (e.g. indicators of performance, budgetary control statements);
- the form in which the information is made available (e.g. hardcopy reports, VDU enquiries);
- the topic coverage, amount and detail of the information provided;
- the frequency with which information is provided and its timing; and
- the dissemination of certain kinds of information to a wider audience (e.g. leaflets, tapes, videos).

This is because information must ultimately be judged in terms of its benefit to the end-user.

With participation of this kind it is also possible to minimise many of the problems end-users are likely to encounter with information produced solely by specialists. Common problems are those relating to:

- comprehension, particularly in respect of information of a quantitative kind (e.g. financial material, statistical measures produced for management control purposes) and information where insufficient account has been taken of the linguistic barriers to effective communication (e.g. official jargon, clinical terminology, complex sentences);
- overload, that is situations where too much information has been provided and, as a result, end-users feel overwhelmed and unable to cope;
- timeliness, with some information losing its value because it is too late for the purpose for which it was intended;
- accuracy, which is far more likely to be challenged where end-users are confronted with messages they do not wish to hear and where they have been excluded from decisions about the subject matter, the conversion process and the mode of presentation; and
- the failure to accommodate the information needs of those for whom English is a second language.[29]

Problems of this kind arise because inevitably specialists find it difficult to engage with the meaning which end-users will put on the information. They cannot put themselves in the position of the end-users and take full account of their interests, concerns and backgrounds.

Ideally, specialists and end-users should regard themselves as partners in a joint enterprise each with their own distinctive contribution. For specialists these include giving advice, suggesting alternative strategies for achieving a given end and assisting with the education and training of end-users. They are also likely to be heavily involved with the installation of data conversion systems and have a key role to play in monitoring their effectiveness and efficiency. The principal contribution of end-users is to identify the purposes that information is meant to serve, which is always likely to be a matter of debate, as well as to ensure that it does in fact meet the intended purposes. In other words, it should provide them with an appropriate basis for action.

However, the mere availability of accurate, timely, concise and effectively presented information does not of itself guarantee that appropriate action will be taken. Information is a necessary but not sufficient condition for change. This depends upon a range of other factors.

Information and Behaviour

Information, formal and informal, is one of the key influences on behaviour at every level. Research demonstrates that the determinants of behaviour could be said to fall into two broad categories. The first includes psychological factors, such as values, prejudices, implicit knowledge and innate conservatism. For example, in community settings it is far more likely that managers who subscribe to the value of equal opportunities will make changes in respect of the delivery of services, as a result of information highlighting gender and racial discrimination, than those who do not. Similarly, members of the lay constituency who place particular value on their privacy and dignity may be reluctant to accept invitations for health screening.[30]

The second category embraces factors of a more practical nature, such as competing pressures, financial constraints, explicit knowledge and political and structural considerations. For example, because of competing pressures on their time, those preoccupied with applications for trust status are less likely to be in a position to respond to formal information suggesting that the contraction of family planning facilities is having an adverse effect on the well-being of clients. Whereas for informal carers, leaflets advertising support services for which a charge is made will have little impact on those with limited incomes. All information received by end-users is subject to a filtering and prioritising process, in which factors of this kind play a part.

Although formal information will certainly increase the knowledge of end-users, a willingness and an ability to take action, on this basis, are far less likely. Indeed: 'There is no direct link, between changes in knowledge, attitudes and behaviour as has often been assumed'.[31] This is confirmed by the authors of a WHO Review of the effectiveness of 150 health education campaigns. 'Increases in knowledge are easy to achieve but measurable changes in attitudes ... (and) in behaviour are comparatively rare.'[32] Although some attempt has been made to measure the effect of health education and promotional materials on the behaviour of the public at large, this area of research is generally underdeveloped. Moreover, little attention has been given to the link between formal information directed at policy makers, managers and clinicians and subsequent organisational change. It is, however, safe to assume that research in this field would yield similar results, namely that it is relatively easy to increase the knowledge of end-users but extremely difficult to change their behaviour.

Despite these conclusions, most health promotion campaigns and efforts to increase and improve the quality of the information available to policy makers, managers and clinicians are based on the assumption that there is a more direct link between formal information and behaviour than actually exists. More specifically, it has been assumed that:

- the recipients of information are primarily rational individuals;
- provided with sound and accurate information about the desirability and need for change they will follow it;
- behavioural change can be secured without any consideration of the social context within which behaviour occurs;[33] and
- explicit knowledge takes precedence over implicit knowledge in the causation of behaviour.

In reality, however, these are spurious assumptions. Individuals do not always behave in what experts, operating on utilitarian principles, would consider to be a rational manner. 'Action is a consequence not solely of cognition but also of that mix of emotion, habit, impulse, bloody-mindedness and lack of forethought which is characteristically human.'[34] Moreover, rationality itself is far from unambiguous. Graham, for example, in discussing the reasons why poor mothers smoke, argues that 'the organisation of family life imposes constraints on the carer ... (and therefore) what constitutes sensible and reasonable behaviour may radically change'.[35] In other words, their behaviour reflects not only external factors but also the implicit knowledge which gives meaning to what they do.

Armed with these insights it is possible to take a number of steps which will at least strengthen the link between information and behaviour. A first step is to ensure that end-users are convinced of the salience of the information and are persuaded by it. This objective can be pursued by a variety of means, of which participation by end-users at every stage of the process by which data are captured and converted into information is likely to be the most effective. With respect to management, interactive styles which acknowledge the 'personhood' of employees, both individually and collectively, will therefore have more chance of being successful than authoritarian styles.[36] For similar reasons, within health promotion, increasing use is being made of anthropological and other techniques which draw upon the implicit knowledge of target groups.[37] Luck and others have demonstrated the importance both of group work in generating lay people's ideas about initiatives (such as smoking cessation courses) and of linking information with the 'process within which information is used.'[38] In the CHSs participation is vital because of the problems involved in producing 'good' information, which reflects in full the nature and complexity of health encounters and other activities.

Second, where the relevance of the 'message' has been established, there is evidence to suggest that repetition, using a variety of methods, helps to sustain changes in behaviour. This can be seen in appraisal and review systems, which involve regular two-way communication between managers and staff and other activities. Likewise, many health promotion strategies do not rely simply on written media but also incorporate activity-based initiatives. In these ways information is internalised and 'the new behaviour ... becomes relegated ... to the routine level'[39] and thereby stands a better chance of being permanent.

Third, training clearly has a part to play in alerting those involved to the manner in which the role of information, as a determinant of behaviour, can be undermined by other factors. For clinicians, managers and policy makers this means access to courses and workshops where they can explore the relative effect of attitudes, beliefs, implicit knowledge, organisational constraints and formal information on their behaviour. In the case of clients, training and educational opportunities arise in a variety of contexts, including self-help and other groups, schools and clinical encounters. It is important to take advantage of these from the point of view not only of sharing information but also of discussing the countervailing influences on behaviour. For example, children should not only be made aware of the adverse effects of certain modes of behaviour but also be encouraged to consider the reasons why such behaviours persist.

Last, everything possible should be done to ensure that 'messages' are not sabotaged by organisational practices and by public policies. If first line managers are to respond positively and imaginatively to information which indicates that there is a high level of work related stress amongst their staff, they need to be assured that their efforts will not be undermined by the actions of middle and senior management which can easily exacerbate the problem. Similarly, in the sphere of health promotion, it is increasingly recognised that, for campaigns to have any chance of success, public policies need to be shaped in such a way that 'healthy choices are the easier choices', both for individuals and organisations (see Chapter 6).

Even where these steps are taken it has to be recognised that the link between formal information and behaviour is stronger in some cases than others. As a result, some changes will always be difficult to achieve. Information is more likely to bring about the desired change in situations where those for whom it is intended are, for various reasons, already in a receptive frame of mind. Recent research has shown that there a number of distinct but related circumstances which might have an effect on the receptivity of the end-user. A traumatic or sudden event might precipitate a review of behaviour. For example, for those engaged in service delivery, this would include threats to employment and status. For the public at large, illness or bereavement is likely to have a similar effect. Similarly, a change in the environment, such as the introduction of psychological testing for managers[40] and the restriction of smoking in public places 'causes some behaviour to become problematic'[41] and existing practices inappropriate. Finally, there can be 'a long process of consideration of some behaviour and a weighing of the pros and cons of changing it'. In this way formal information, such as that relating to the philosophy and value of group work in health visiting or to the ill effects of alcohol, will be effective only in situations where extensive thought has already been given to the behaviour in question.

Although these circumstances can contribute in a positive way to changes in behaviour, they can equally well create a climate which is hostile. To be effective formal information needs to be compatible with the experiences, circumstances and values of those concerned. Where this is not the case information may well be subject to the charge that it is being used as propaganda. For example, some of the promotional material produced in support of *Working for Patients* was felt by many to be designed more to indoctrinate than to inform managers and service providers. Similarly, AIDS campaigns have been criticised on the grounds that they 'are not purely informational, let alone educational, since they give a slanted message designed to manipulate and persuade. They are ambitious attempts at a new form of mass social engineering.'[42]

In seeking to change behaviour through the use of information, it is incumbent upon all those involved to take account of these factors. Moreover, it must be recognised that the owners of information are in a powerful position and should therefore be accountable for the manner in which they discharge their information function.

The Ownership of Information

In view of the fact that formal information is a political resource, its ownership can be the subject of dispute. For the CHSs issues concerning ownership are of fundamental importance for a variety of reasons.

First, relevant information is likely to be dispersed. If they are to function effectively, many CHSs staff require information about named individuals, which may be held by members of other professional groups within their own agency or within other agencies. The quality of care depends 'inter alia' upon the willingness of all those involved to keep each other fully informed. For example, frail elderly people often have a wide variety of needs which are likely to be met adequately only if district nurses, chiropodists, physiotherapists, GPs, home helps and those responsible for meals on wheels and other services are prepared to share information with one another. Similarly, the continuity of care for patients discharged from institutions depends upon an adequate flow of information across the hospital-community divide. A failure to share information may be due to either professional possessiveness or the absence of adequate procedures for this purpose.

Second, various agencies are engaged in the planning and delivery of community based health care. Therefore, information often serves as a bargaining counter in the complex inter-agency negotiations and collaborative enterprises which characterise community health care. This gives rise to a number of questions. For example, should data collected or information produced by one agency to meet a particular need be made available to another agency for a different purpose?

A good illustration of this issue is provided by the lengthy negotiations which have surrounded attempts to make the patient registration data held by FHSAs more widely available.[43] Significantly, from the point of view of the CHSs, in 1990 the DH reached the conclusion that 'it is in the interest of every person registered under the NHS that DHAs should have available the most accurate information possible'. To this end, family practitioner committees (FPCs), now FHSAs, were instructed to 'take the necessary steps for releasing such information to DHAs'. However, in recognition of the sensitive nature of this issue, strict conditions were imposed in respect of the uses to which the information could be put. For example, 'use of the information should be confined to NHS purposes. These include care and treatment, management, planning and audit.'[44] In short, agencies must be prepared to share information in the interests of improving the quality of care.

Third, the ownership of information carries with it a range of responsibilities with regard to confidentiality, privacy, accessibility and security, which are more difficult to exercise in community settings. Again this is largely because of the dispersed nature of the information concerned.

The importance of these matters was underlined in the guidance on the preparation of information strategies, which was issued by the NHS Management Board in 1987.

> *Strategies will need to specify the means for ensuring that confidentiality and data protection considerations pervade all systems development. Policies for dealing with data protection laws, subject access, release of data to external bodies and treatment of "small numbers" should be clearly stated.*[45]

Such guidance is becoming even more pertinent in the CHSs with the moves towards the development of more comprehensive databases containing a wealth of detailed and highly personal information. Ironically, however, this trend will make it increasingly difficult to ensure adequate protection for individuals. The dangers of accidental disclosure and the temptation to use information for income generation purposes will multiply.

Last, in performing their health promotion role, CHSs staff are often inhibited because they have to rely on the release of information which is owned by others. Sadly, but not surprisingly, whether or not complete information enters the public domain 'seems to depend upon the advantage of concealment or revelation to vested interests'[46] rather than the contribution which its disclosure might make to the health of the public at large. For example, whereas the risk factors said to be associated with a susceptibility to heart disease are well publicised, 'the doubt which attends these so-called risk factors is scarcely known to the general public at all.'[47]

Even though there are no easy answers to questions surrounding the ownership and other aspects of information, they need to be addressed systematically. Information, as a resource, is too important to be left to chance, the vagaries of passing fashion or individual prejudices.

Towards a Systematic Approach to Information and its Management

Traditionally, little attention has been given by those responsible for the planning and delivery of community based health care services to the design of the information systems needed to support these activities and to the development of a systematic and integrated approach to the management of information. This has been due, in part, to a marked reluctance on the part of service managers and health care professionals to contemplate the sharing of information. Consequently, systems for recording and storing information about clients and their needs have tended to evolve in a somewhat haphazard and piecemeal manner with each service, such as pre-school child health, school health, district nursing, community psychiatric nursing, chiropody and speech therapy, going its own way. Thus, systems have rarely been compatible with one another and very little information has been transferred from one system to another, with the result that where clients have been in receipt of more than one service their personal details have been held on more than one system. Clearly this is inefficient.

In some respects, the fragmentation which has characterised information systems in the past is still very much in evidence, and the introduction of IT has simply been used as an opportunity to convert manual systems into electronic ones rather than to develop a more integrated and sophisticated approach to the management of information. Moreover, attempts to rationalise the situation have sometimes made matters worse. For example, the recommendations relating to community based health care services in the fifth report of the Korner Working Party, which were ostensibly designed to enable CHSs managers to develop a more coherent approach to information management have often resulted in authorities developing non-patient based information systems alongside their client based systems. Thus, many community units/trusts now have three major systems. One is for child health, which is client based and was often the first to be computerised; another is for other services, which is again client based; and the third is a Korner information system, which is activity based. Consequently, systems remain fragmented and much needs to be done.

The pressures for the application of a more systematic and comprehensive approach to information and its management arise from a number of sources. These include:

- the development of needs assessment and business planning in conjunction with the moves towards a contractual relationship between the commissioners and providers of services (see Chapter 5) and securing better 'value for money' in the delivery of services;
- the importance of targeting 'at risk' groups for screening and other health promotion purposes and small area health profiling studies;
- the desire to erode traditional boundaries between services, including those provided by GPs, which have often been reinforced by having separate and distinctive information systems, as a step towards a more integrated approach to service delivery and the establishment of more effective mechanisms for intersectoral working and the securing of a seamless web of care;
- the moves towards greater participation by members of the lay constituency in decisions relating to their own health and that of the communities to which they belong (see Chapter 6); and
- the wish to make the public at large more aware of the services available in the interests of promoting equal access and facilitating consumer choice.

Significantly, many such pressures can be directly related to the 'crisis in health' (see Chapter 1).

In response to them, a number of important initiatives have been taken. First, most units and trusts with responsibility for the CHSs have appointed information officers and established information departments, to take the lead in designing and developing systems.

Although there are dangers in this approach, with information being perceived as yet another specialist function, it is generally accepted that for progress to be made in this sphere, leadership from those with appropriate expertise is essential. However, as indicated earlier, serious problems can arise from the appointment of technical specialists who have little knowledge of health issues. This situation calls for more courses along the lines of those pioneered by Jeannette Murphy, which successfully integrate IT with health policy.[48]

Second, IT is increasingly being used to facilitate the conversion of operational data (e.g. relating to individual episodes of care) into management information (e.g. relating to the costs of treatment and staff deployment) and the development of a more integrated approach to the organisation and use of information. In order to maintain the momentum in this respect: 'The next generation of operational systems will need to be capable of providing common index and scheduling functions so that information can be produced which allows the tracking of all a patient's contacts with health professionals during an episode of care.'[49]

Third, many CHSs managers have prepared an information strategy as an integral part of their business plans. According to McArthur and Stone, the key ingredients of such a strategy are 'a definition of the principles which will underpin future developments, a 'vision' for the future, and a description of the various elements of that vision in practical terms.'[50] Within community units/trusts these elements are likely to include:

- a management information system, which will integrate activity data with that relating to the utilisation of resources;
- a population/environmental profile, which 'will serve as a central system for collecting and aggregating data about the population served and sub-sets of the population';[51] and
- a community index or population health register,[52] which will eventually contain details of every individual for whom the unit/trust has responsibility.

In the long run it is likely to be the development of the community index which will have the most far-reaching implications for the community as a whole. As the information it contains becomes more detailed and comprehensive, so its potential as an instrument for the fine tuning of health promotion activities will increase. This, however, is unlikely to be universally welcomed. It will be perceived by many as yet another threat to their liberty and privacy and as undermining the 'personhood' of individuals and groups by allowing for more effective social control.

Last, in some areas efforts are being made to increase and improve the flow of information to all those with an interest in health, including clients and the public at large. A good example of what can be done in this respect is provided by the Health Information Project undertaken in the the Northern Region. The project was funded by the British Library Research and Development Department and its aims were:

- 'To establish the extent and range of health provision to the community in the Northern Region and to identify the agencies involved in its provision.
- To achieve a description and definition of community health information in the context of a health information plan and to identify issues for the co-ordination and future development of health information to the community.
- To propose a framework for the improved delivery of health information in the community.'[53]

It was led by Susan Childs, a specialist in health information.

Significantly, community health information was defined, for the purposes of the project, as 'health and social information that enables individuals to be responsible for their health and well-being and helps them to participate in services for care, treatment and prevention.'[54] Such a definition clearly reflects the multidimensionality of information and the contribution which it can make to strengthening the position of the lay constituency. However, it is very individualistic in its orientation and does not incorporate the notion of empowering communities, which has been at the heart of many exciting developments in the sphere of health promotion both in this country and elsewhere.[55]

Underpinning all these initiatives is the emergence, in some districts, of what could be described as an 'information culture'. The principal features of this are a recognition of the value of information both as a management resource and as a means of enabling individuals and communities to become more fully involved in the health process; a belief in the efficacy of shared information; and a willingness to learn how to make the best use of information. It is also essential that in such a culture due regard is given to informal information and implicit knowledge, if the narrowness and sterility of the utilitarian view is to be avoided.[56]

Even where the culture is supportive, in making decisions about information and its management, it is vital for CHSs staff to adhere to a number of fundamental principles. Of crucial importance is the need for the design of information and related systems to be firmly based on the principle of participation by data capturers, end-users and clients alike. Evidence suggests that where this principle is applied, systems will be client based, fully accessible, integrated and flexible and will meet the needs of professional groups and incorporate adequate arrangements for training.

Likewise, the production of information must never be seen as an end in its itself, but always as a means to an end. Arguably, for those committed to the cause of community health care the most important of these ends are more effective management and service delivery; greater discernment on the part of clients; the adoption of healthier lifestyles by the public at large; and greater confidence on their part to construct healthier environments.

Moreover, 'there must be realism about what is achievable and, in particular, about the resources and time required to achieve it.'[57] In the past a considerable amount of damage has been caused by the unrealistic expectations engendered by the more extravagant claims of some IT specialists and software houses. Everything possible should be done to avoid this happening in the future. For example, steps should be taken to ensure a high degree of information and computer 'literacy' on the part of end-users and those responsible for making decisions about the purchase of equipment and the design of information systems.

Last, with regard to information dissemination, high priority should be given to the principle of openness. Although information about individuals must be subject to safeguards, the onus should always be on those who wish to limit access to justify their position.

Application of these principles will ensure that information makes a more significant contribution to the future development of community health care than would otherwise be the case. Similarly, strategies designed to empower front line service providers and lay people, through the legitimisation of the implicit knowledge which they bring to health encounters, will enrich the care provided in community settings and will avoid the dangers inherent in equating information with explicit knowledge.

Notes

1 For further details, see A. Squires (ed.), *Multicultural Healthcare and Rehabilitation of Older People* (London: Age Concern/Edward Arnold, 1991).

2 For further information about people with disabilities, see J. Martin, H. Meltzer and D. Elliot, *OPCS Surveys of Disability in Great Britain. Report 1: The Prevalence of Disability Among Adults* (London: HMSO, 1988). In seeking to identify and classify those with disabilities they follow the WHO's guidance, on which the International Classification of Impairments and Handicaps is based. This distinguishes between: 'impairment' (i.e. problems with the structure or function of parts of the body, such as arthritis); 'disability', which involves ordinary daily activities (e.g. walking a given distance at a given pace) and 'handicap' meaning restriction of role function in a way which disadvantages the individual (e.g. the difficulty of getting a suitable job due to inaccessible transport or discriminatory recruitment practices). J. Martin et.al. treat disability as being on a continuum and note that people with disabilities point to ways in which the environment rather than their impairment prevents them from taking a full part in social life. This implies that doctors with special knowledge of impairments are not necessarily in the best position to make assessments.

3 See, for example, M. Stacey, *The Sociology of Health and Healing* (London: Unwin Hyman, 1988), esp. chs.10-12; many of the articles in S. Cunningham-Burley and N. McKeganey (eds.), *Readings in Medical Sociology* (London: Routledge, 1990); P. Barham and R. Hayward, *From the Mental Patient to the Person* (London: Routledge, 1991); and M. Oliver, *Social Work. Disabled People and Disabling Environments* (London: J. Kingsley, 1991).

4 The National Association of Health Authorities, *NHS Handbook*, 4th Edition (London: Macmillan Reference Books, 1989), p.73.

5 A. Chandor with J. Graham and R. Williamson, *A Dictionary of Computers* (London: Penguin Books, 1970), p.99.

6 I. Powell and D. Prothero, 'Sticking to Korner', *The Health Service Journal*, 28 April 1988, p.484.

7 G. Best, 'Performance indicators: a precautionary tale for managers', in I. Wickings (ed.), *Effective Unit Management* (London: King's Fund Publishing Office, 1983), pp.17-18.

8 DHSS, Health Notice HN(86)34, *Health Services Management: Resource Management (Management Budgeting) in Health Authorities,* November 1986.

9 According to Department of Health, *Working for Patients: Developing Districts* (London: HMSO, 1990):
'A substantial range of information is potentially available to support (the)

assessment process. But much of this information is difficult to interpret and only relates indirectly to the assessment of health need in a way that can inform the contracting process.

Nevertheless information about incidence and prevalence (e.g. by sex, age and condition), linked with that about the evaluation of different interventions does offer scope for development of a population based approach to the assessment of health needs' (paras.2.8 and 2.9).

10 DH, *The Health of the Nation. A Consultative Document for Health in England*, Cmd 1527 (London: HMSO, 1991). It is worrying, but not surprising, that in this document health targets are conceived solely in terms of explicit knowledge and formal information. For example, targets should be 'explicit, quantified and monitorable over time through appropriate indicators'. Moreover, although it is proposed that each health authority should determine its own quality of service targets, thereby providing scope for the use of implicit knowledge, the one example provided, namely appointment times, is clearly based on explicit knowledge.

11 For further details of most of these initiatives and their impact on the CHSs, see R. Ottewill and A. Wall, *The Growth and Development of the Community Health Services* (Sunderland: Business Education Publishers, 1990), esp. pp.261-2, 273-4 and 364-9.

12 Powell and Prothero, op.cit.

13 J. Naish and R. Kline, 'What counts can't always be counted', *Health Visitor*, vol.63, no.12, December 1990, p.421.

14 See, for example, DHSS, *Neighbourhood Nursing. A Focus for Care* [Cumberlege Report] (London: HMSO, 1986) in which the point is made that: 'Community nurses spend much of their time routinely collecting data on their caseloads and workloads, but they and their managers have little use for the management information which may be produced from it' (p.11).

15 M. McArthur and S. Stone, 'Information use in effective community management' in A. McNaught (ed.), *Managing Community Health Services* (London: Chapman and Hall, 1991), p.48.

16 See J. Naish and R. Kline, op.cit.

17 Powell and Prothero, op.cit.

18 See Chapter 5 for a more detailed discussion of the role of information in planning.

19 The specification of health targets by health districts has been prompted, in the main, by the WHO European Strategy targets (see Chapters 1 and 6 for further details) and the subsequent Healthy Cities Project.

20 OPCS publications of particular value include:
Key population and vital statistics: local and health authority areas.
General Household Survey reports.
Communicable disease statistics.

21 Computing News, *The Health Service Journal,* 9 August 1990, p.1167.

22 J. Cornwell, *The Consumers' View: Elderly People and Community Health Services* (London: King's Fund Centre for Health Services Development, 1989), p.9.

23 For further details of information of this kind, see A. Bowling, *Measuring Health: A review of quality of life scales* (Milton Keynes: Open University Press, 1991).

24 M. McArthur and S. Stone, op.cit., p.51.

25 For further details of what can be achieved in this respect, see D. Avison and P. Catchpole, 'Unconventional Korner', *The Health Service Journal*, 23 June 1988, pp.704-5. In this article Avison and Catchpole evaluate the role played by community health care professionals in designing a multipurpose information system for Darlington Health Authority.

26 Ibid.

27 Croydon Community Health Trust, *Trust Application*, p.33.

28 B. Lattimer and A. Mason, *Information for Action* (London: The Institute of Health Services Management, undated), p.25.

29 To appreciate the significance of this point with respect to community health initiatives see A. McNaught, *Health Action and Ethnic Minorities* (London: Bedford Square Press, 1987). For the service implications, see T.S. Ananthanarayanan, 'Cultural factors in the organisation of a psychogeriatric service for elderly Asians in North Staffordshire' in J. Cox and S. Bostock (eds.), *Racial Discrimination in the Health Service* (Newcastle under Lyme: Penrhos, 1989).

30 For a summary of the results of a survey undertaken by a research team at the Christie Hospital, Manchester, into the reasons why women did not attend screening sessions, see *NHS Management Bulletin*, April 1989.

31 P. Bennett, C. Smith, Z. Nugent and C. Panter, '"Psst ... the really useful guide to alcohol": evaluation of an alcohol education television series', *Health Education Research: Theory & Practice,* vol.6 no.1, 1991.

32 Quoted in an article by D. Anderson, 'Facts and figures that damn the AIDS campaign charade', *The Sunday Times*, 21 October 1990.

33 See Research Unit in Health and Behavioural Change, University of Edinburgh, *Changing the Public Health* (Chichester: J. Wiley and Sons, 1989).

34 Ibid, p.67.

35 H. Graham, *Women, Health and the Family* (London: Wheatsheaf Books, 1985), p.173.

36 For a detailed discussion of management/leadership styles, see C. Handy, *Understanding Organisations*, 3rd Edition (London: Penguin, 1985), ch.4.

37 For example, in developing a health related behaviour questionnaire for use in schools, John Balding (School Health Education Unit, University of Exeter) has taken seriously the need for young people to express their own understandings of their behaviour and to provide them with an opportunity of comparing themselves with others in nearby schools. Health promotion curriculum planning initiatives have been based on his findings. For further details, see J. Balding, *The Provision of Health Care at Community Level*, Croydon Community Health Trust Health Needs Assessment Workshop, 1991, unpublished.

38 M. Luck, *A Manual of Market Research for Health Promotion* (Birmingham: West Midlands RHA, 1991), p.4.

39 Research Unit in Health and Behavioural Change, op.cit., p.85.

40 For further details of the NHS Management Executive's plans to 'audit' health service managers every three to five years, with the help of psychological tests to determine whether they possesss the skills and attributes they need to perform their duties, see news item in *The Health Service Journal*, 7 March 1991, p.3.

41 Research Unit in Health and Behavioural Change, op.cit., p.84.

42 D. Anderson, op.cit.

43 For details of some of the arguments used by the various interested parties, see R. Ottewill and A. Wall, op.cit., pp.402-3.

44 DH, Circular HC(FP)(90)10, *Guidelines for the Release of Patient Registration Data by Family Practitioner Committees to District Health Authorities*, undated.

45 *Information Management in the Hospital and Community Services: Guidance for Information Strategies*, July 1987, p.28.

46 Research Unit in Health and Behavioural Change, op.cit., p.155.

47 Ibid.

48 Now senior lecturer at St Bartholomew's Hospital. She developed these courses while at the Polytechnic of North London.

49 B. Lattimer and A. Mason, op.cit., p.29.

50 M. McArthur and S. Stone, op.cit., p.64.

51 Ibid.

52 Work on the development of a population health register is being undertaken by a number of commissioning authorities, such as Sheffield Health Authority, using funds from the DH DISP (Developing Information

Systems for Purchasers) programme for this purpose. According to the *Project Initiation Document* produced for the Sheffield Health Information Project, the register will provide a 'complete base for constructing survey sampling frames (that can) be used for obtaining community views on aspects of health' and will facilitate the 'mapping of population age groups'. Other potential uses include outcome studies; the measurement of service usage, according to disability status, ethnicity, gender etc; and needs analysis. The extent to which registers of this kind are used by providing, as opposed to commissioning, agencies remains to be seen.

53 S. Childs, *Health Information Services to the Community in the Northern Region* (Newcastle upon Tyne: Information North, 1990a), p.2. See also, S. Childs, *Health Information in the High Street* (Newcastle upon Tyne: Information North, 1990b). Similar principles are being applied in the National Disability Information Project, the aims of which are to improve disability information services through the development of a national framework, more integrated local services, and improved common information networks.

54 S. Childs (1990a), op.cit., p.2.

55 For a detailed discussion of this kind of development see, N. Wallerstein, 'Powerlessness, Empowerment and Health: Implications for health promotion programs', *American Journal of Health Promotion*, vol.6(3), Jan/Feb 1992.

56 L. Doyal and I Gough, *A Theory of Human Need* (London: Macmillan, 1991), make a similar point using slightly different language: 'Need-satisfaction is more than the top-down application of technical knowledge and the bureaucratic delivery of state services ... There is another domain of understanding to be tapped - the experiential knowledge of people in their ordinary lives: as workers, residents in a community, patients, pupils, older citizens, parents, immigrants etc' (p.299). An example of the dangers of relying exclusively on formal information is provided in S. Lonsdale, *Women and Disability: the experience of physical disability among women* (Basingstoke: Macmillan Education, 1990). She draws attention to the fact that many women with disabilities felt that they had not been properly consulted and that as a result their understanding of their needs had not been 'incorporated into the ... process of health care.'

57 B. Lattimer and A. Mason, op.cit., p.39.

CHAPTER 5

Planning and Commissioning

Application of the founding values of the NHS namely: universality, comprehensiveness, equality and a service free at the point of use (see Chapter 2), implies a necessity for planning. Significantly, however, it was not until the 1960s that formal recognition was given to the importance of planning for the realisation of these values. The delay was primarily due to two concerns, finance and organisation, which preoccupied policy makers in the early years of the NHS. These have proved to be endemic and continue to bedevil those engaged in planning. Thus, despite major changes both in the method of allocating resources and in the structure of the NHS, service-led planning initiatives taken by the centre remain hostage to economic and political fortune.

Early initiatives included the Ministry of Health's requirement in 1962 that every local health authority should prepare ten year plans for the long-term development of their health and welfare services;[1] the establishment of the NHS planning system; the introduction of joint planning; and the implementation of the recommendations of the Resource Allocation Working Party (RAWP) in 1976.[2] Equally important for the CHSs were the attempts by the Department of Health and Social Security (DHSS) to set service objectives, such as the publication of *Priorities for Health and Social Services in England* (1976); the report of the Committee on Child Health Services, *Fit for the Future* (1976), and *Prevention and Health: Everybody's Business* (1976).[3]

More recent initiatives include: making DHAs (and other agencies) responsible for identifying the needs of their resident population and ensuring that these needs are met;[4] the planning regime for community care introduced under the provisions of the National Health Service and Community Care Act 1990;[5] and the move towards the setting of explicit health targets at national level.[6] The last of these underlines the distinction which is increasingly being made between planning for health services and planning for health (see Chapter 6).

Whereas service-led planning, almost by definition, leaves in place the existing pattern of services, planning for health with its emphasis on setting targets and asking fundamental questions about the determinants of health could well be favourable to the CHSs. This is because of their broad remit and the contribution which they make to health promotion.

At the same time, there has a been a shift of emphasis within service planning, from that which is provider-led to that which is finance-led. This involves examining the relationship between the cost of services and the effectiveness of their outcomes and there is evidence to suggest that the community based services fare well when cost-benefit analyses of this kind are undertaken. It also, somewhat paradoxically, opens up possibilities for including a broader range of factors in the planning process and this too is likely to be advantageous to the CHSs.

Every type of planning is a way of securing a more purposeful and systematic approach to, and of injecting greater certainty into, the development of policies and the delivery of services. In essence, it is an iterative process embracing a variety of related activities. These include:

- negotiating a suitable framework;
- assessing and measuring various aspects of the current position, such as needs, demands, threats and opportunities (i.e. Where are we now?);
- determining a desired future state, in terms of goals, aims, objectives, targets, (i.e. Where do we want to be?);
- generating and evaluating alternative ways of achieving this desired future state (i.e. How do we get from where we are now to where we want to be?);
- making arrangements for the implementation of the most favoured options;
- monitoring progress towards the realisation of the desired future state; and
- whenever necessary, taking corrective action.

In this way, it is possible to place decision making on a more secure foundation and to eliminate gaps, avoid unnecessary duplication, target resources and exploit opportunities.

Within health care there has been a strong emphasis on comprehensive or normative planning, on which the NHS planning system was originally based. This involved the establishment of complex procedures and systems in an attempt to secure professionally determined standards of health care; the commitment of members of the key constituencies; and a more efficient and equitable distribution of resources. In recent years there has been a move towards a more commercially oriented approach, incorporating aspects of business planning.[7] The adoption of this approach by community and other NHS units/trusts has been prompted, in the main, by a shift in the climate and the need to secure service contracts in a situation where competition is being encouraged and explicitly used as the 'driving force for change', with resources going to the 'best' service providers.[8] At the same time, a modified version of normative planning offers a coherent framework within which DHAs and, to some extent, other agencies can exercise their commissioning (purchasing)[9] and contracting responsibilities. Figure 5.1. illustrates the coexistence of normative planning with business planning and the distinction between the commissioners and the providers of health care.

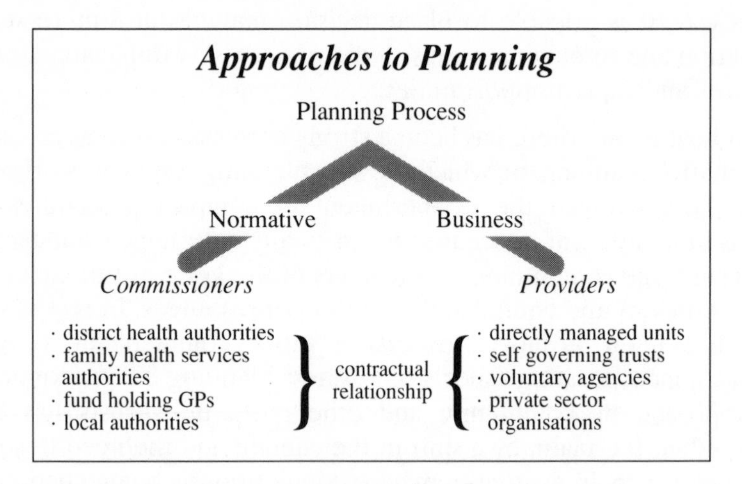

Figure 5.1

Notes

a. Although the functions of FHSAs incorporate aspects of both purchasing and providing, according to Duncan Nichol, from the NHS Management Executive's perspective, 'they fall within the purchaser category as commissioning partners with DHAs.'

b. Of the fifty six first wave trusts, which became operational on 1st April 1991, the following five had previously been community units:

Chester and Halton Community Trust,
Cornwall Primary and Community Health,
Croydon Community Health,
First Community Health (Mid-Stafforshire Community Health Unit),
West Dorset Community Services.

Another ten first wave trusts included CHSs amongst their responsibilities. These were:

Anglian Harbours Health Trust (CHSs, mental health and handicap services),
Central Manchester Health Authority (all services)
East Gloucestershire NHS Trust (all services)
East Somerset Trust (all services)
North West Herts Priority Health Services (CHSs, mental health and handicap services)
Rugby District Services (all services)
South Devon Healthcare Trust (all services)
Taunton and Somerset NHS Trust (all services)
United Bristol Heathcare Trust (all services)
Weston Health Services Trust (all services)

Despite these developments, in practice it has proved to be extremely difficult, to apply fully the principles of planning to health and social care services. This can be accounted for in a number of ways.

First, there are the pressures, uncertainties and contradictions arising from the turbulent economic, clinical, technological and political environment, and the shifting demographic and epidemiological context within which services of this kind are provided. As indicated in Chapter 1, in recent years the turbulence has become so great that many now argue that there is a fundamental 'crisis in health'. In some respects recent initiatives in planning, especially those involving changes in the way that services are managed, can be seen as a response to the financial aspects of the 'crisis'. It is therefore somewhat ironic that other aspects have played a significant part in creating formidable problems for those involved in the planning process. For example, growing concern over the impact of the environment on health has meant that a far wider range of agencies and professions have to be involved in planning CHSs, with all the logistic and other hurdles that this implies.

Second, the shift to an overt and systematic assessment of needs, which lies at the heart of the comprehensive or normative approach to planning, has raised fundamental conceptual and moral issues which must be addressed in a more honest and open manner than they have been. In the past, insofar as needs have been assessed, the medical sub-constituency has been in the driving seat. However, it now has to be recognised that need assessment is a complex matter.[10] Very difficult choices have to be made in respect of prioritising needs and the deployment of resources to meet them and no single constituency has a monopoly of wisdom in resolving the moral predicaments to which these choices give rise (see Chapter 2).

Third, it is extremely difficult to undertake the description of services needed for planning purposes. This is the case even in the best of circumstances and in community settings it is even more so. The reasons for this are that services in the community are less visible, geographically dispersed and their boundaries unclear. Thus, inputs, such as staff time, and processes, such as counselling, are more difficult to delineate. Moreover, a greater variety of agencies and professional groups are likely to be involved.[11]

Fourth, for similar reasons, the implementation of plans for community based health care services presents more difficulties than those for institutionally based services. Additionally, in an environment where the principle of professional autonomy remains firmly entrenched, the intentions of the planners may well be thwarted by service deliverers. This is particularly likely to be the case where members of the clinical constituency feel alienated from the planning process; do not share the goals and values of the planners; and have no sense of ownership. Arguably, this will remain the case even where those implementing plans have a contractual relationship with those who prepare them.

Fifth, the planning process and mechanisms for allocating resources have tended to develop in parallel. Whereas both have been considered important, they have never been fully integrated. For example, in 1976 the NHS planning system and RAWP were established independently. As Hunter argues: 'For planning to be meaningful, it is essential to establish close links between plans and resources.'[12] The development of commissioning and business planning, may well serve to bring the two closer together, but this is an issue that will need to be constantly addressed. One reason for this is the tension between the high expectations of the clinical and lay constituencies and the restraining hand of the managerial constituency.

Last, information systems, which are an essential prerequisite for effective planning, have never been sufficiently robust or comprehensive to begin to meet the needs of planners. Whatever planning framework is being used, the production, analysis and manipulation of information holds the key to its successful application. Furthermore, as indicated in Chapter 4, information strategies are even less well developed for CHSs than they are for HSs and comparatively little attention has been given to employing the implicit knowledge of service users, carers and staff and to establishing sound methodologies of outcome measurement.

In writing about the preparations for the introduction of the 'new style' NHS in East Anglia, the Director of Service Purchasing at Cambridge Health Authority commented that: 'Better information is vital for the successful (operation) of (an) internal market. Purchasers need to know the services provided for their resident population. Providers need to be able to assign all services provided to a contract, and to invoice accordingly.'[13] These considerations will apply whatever the nature of the relationship between commissioners and providers.

Thus, the principles enunciated at the end of the previous chapter regarding information and its management are of particular relevance for both planning and commissioning. However, although the developments discussed in Chapter 4 offer some hope for the future, again a note of caution needs to be struck. Since information is a costly resource, without a substantial investment of time and money, progress is likely to lag behind the aspirations of those engaged in the planning and commissioning processes.

For the CHSs these considerations are exacerbated by the fact that it is impossible to plan effectively without taking account of what is happening elsewhere. As pointed out in Chapter 1, community health care is an integral part of a far wider health and social care system. Thus, any attempts to plan on a unilateral basis are doomed to failure. Moreover, although health authorities may have had separate health care (or care group) planning teams for acute services and for mentally ill, mentally handicapped and elderly people, they have not done so for community based services which cut across these areas. Consequently, in the words of Marks and her colleagues: 'Relevant to each, (they were) the focus of none.'[14] Added to this are the uncertainties arising from the moves towards increased 'pluralism' and greater commercialisation and competition in health care. As Kemp argues: 'Contracting has heightened awareness of the purchaser/provider split and emphasised the difference of interests between them. The purchaser has to control expenditure against cash limits: the provider is interested in increasing income.'[15] Thus, those committed to the CHSs will have to make strenuous efforts and be constantly vigilant to ensure that they are not marginalised by planners.

It is now the intention to examine, from the perspective of community health care, some of the issues surrounding:

- the comprehensive or normative approach to planning;
- business planning; and
- the integrated planning of primary care and community care services.

Normative/Comprehensive Planning

As mentioned earlier, it is the normative or comprehensive approach which underpinned the NHS planning system established in 1976. Based on the so-called rational model of decision making, which is particularly associated with Herbert Simon, it comprises 'a logical, systematic and thorough sequence of steps which aims to take everything into account and give due weight to all possible considerations'[16]. In the classic formulation of the rational decision making process these steps are:

- identification, measurement and assessment of needs/problems; 

- setting short-term and long-term objectives in relation to these needs/problems;
- generation and evaluation of alternative strategies for achieving these objectives;
- implementation of the chosen strategy; and
- monitoring, review and control of performance.

Clearly, at each stage of the process, access to an adequate supply of relevant information is of paramount importance.

The influence of the normative approach is clearly reflected in the key elements of the NHS planning system, which covered the CHSs, as well as the HSs. These elements were:

- the strategic plan, incorporating the results of a five yearly assessment of current conditions, perceived needs, policies and goals for the following years;
- the annual programme, containing the implementation proposals for the year ahead; and
- the annual review, for assessing progress and performance and identifying priorities for the next planning round.

In view of the hierarchical nature of the NHS it was also felt necessary to build into the system a degree of vertical integration to ensure that, as far as possible, agencies at each level had the same priorities and goals. Thus, regional health authorities (RHAs), DHAs and units were required to plan and give an account of their performance within a framework set by the agency above them in the hierarchy.

With the moves towards competition and the distinction between the commissioners and the providers of services, the NHS planning system no longer occupies centre stage as it did in the late 1970s and early 1980s. Nevertheless, certain aspects of the comprehensive or normative approach remain influential, especially with respect to the exercise by DHAs of their public health and commissioning responsibilities.

Following the Acheson Report, *Public Health in England* (1988), the government issued a circular requiring DHAs 'to identify the total health care needs of (their) population(s) and plan how these should be met ... in the light of national policies ... local priorities and resources.'[17] Not only was this a 'comprehensive ... statement of national policy', but also, by distinguishing between policy aims and service objectives, it began the process of differentiating between health and health care. A further step in this direction was taken in 1991 with the publication of the Green Paper, *The Health of the Nation* (see Chapter 6).

At the same time, in performing their commissioning role, which dates from 1991, DHAs are expected to place 'a co-ordinated series of contracts with selected providers and ... monitor them.' The process is intended to be a dynamic one, with regular updating and modification of plans to reflect changing needs and circumstances.[18]

Both public health and commissioning responsibilities place a heavy emphasis on the **assessment of health care needs**. The identification and measurement of need is, however, far from new. Indeed, it provides the rationale for all forms of publically provided welfare, including health care. As Titmuss pointed out in the 1960s 'all collectively provided services are deliberately designed to meet certain socially recognised 'needs'.'[19] Despite its importance, the concept of need has proved to be both elusive and intangible. The development of tools for measuring need, such as indicators of chronic sickness and service outcome, has been slow. As a result, values, including normative judgements made by professionals, have continued to play a large part. In short, need assessment 'is a task almost without limit in terms of both scale and conceptual complexity.'[20]

Consequently, demand has frequently been used as a proxy for need. For example, the managers of community based services, like speech therapy and chiropody, have traditionally assessed the need for them on the basis of the number of referrals, length of waiting lists and waiting times. This is likely to result in an underestimation, since not everyone will express their need in this way. It also produces a distorted picture, in the sense that those in greatest need may be least able to express it. Moreover, with a few exceptions, demand is essentially a response to existing services. In other words, rather than defining need in an absolute sense, demand largely reflects decisions about service provision which have already been made. Clearly, with the more explicit responsibility for need assessment which DHAs and other agencies are now required to exercise, new ways must be found of addressing past difficulties in this respect. As Charlwood argues: 'While health authorities have had well-established service planning functions for many years, the requirement to determine the health needs of the population implies a level of sophistication far greater than many have achieved so far.'[21] This means, in effect, that DHAs must give a high priority to the development and application of appropriate expertise.

It is generally assumed that much of this expertise will be found in public health departments. 'Although the focus may have shifted, the concept of health needs as a prerequisite for effective action is familiar to public health medicine'.[22] Thus, in many districts, specialists in public health have taken responsibility for organising and co-ordinating the assessment of health care needs, as well as advising managers on the range and quality of services required to meet these needs and the determination of priorities. They have also sought to ensure that full recognition is given to the distinctive health care needs of particular sections of the population, such as members of ethnic minority communities,[23] women, the homeless and those living in socially deprived areas, and to the assessment of need for health promotion and disease prevention services.[24] Key documents in this respect have been the annual health reports of the directors of public health (DsPH). Indeed, Sir Donald Acheson (Chief Medical Officer 1984–1991), indicated that one of the main purposes of these reports was 'to be an integral component of the health planning and contracting cycle informing priorities and service specifications' (see Chapter 6).[25]

However, accurate assessment of health care needs will never be an easy task. Measurement can be undertaken only when agreement has been reached regarding the definition of need and this is difficult because most health problems, particularly those found in community settings, are neither clear nor unequivocal. An elderly person's need for district nursing or a secondary school's need for an AIDS education programme are examples which contrast starkly with the need for an appendectomy or renal dialysis.

Buchan and Gray, in paraphrasing the DH's definition of need, suggest that 'people in need of a health service (could be) defined as those for whom an intervention produces a benefit at reasonable risk and acceptable cost.'[26] In time-honoured tradition this definition raises as many questions as it answers. Of particular importance is the question of who should be involved in judging what constitutes a 'reasonable risk' and an 'acceptable cost'. While clinicians, such as specialists in public health, and managers have a key role to play in this respect, it is also essential to draw upon the implicit knowledge and expertise of front line service providers and members of the lay constituency.

If agreement is reached regarding the definition then attention can be turned to the measurement of need. This involves the calculation of both incidence, that is the number of new cases occuring over a particular period of time, and prevalence, that is the total number of people displaying the condition in a given population at one point in time. Their relative importance will depend upon the nature of the problem. For example, in order to predict the likely need for health visitor intervention in cases of child abuse, incidence is more important; whereas for chronic conditions, such as diabetes and arthritis, where inputs from district nurses and paramedical staff are likely to be required, knowledge of prevalence would be of more use to planners. However, despite the best efforts of those involved, knowledge of the incidence and prevalence of any health problem can never be complete.

Another consideration is the natural history of the condition in question. Factors which should be considered in this respect are:

- the possible consequences of leaving the condition untreated, which may result in greater demands being placed on service providers in the long-run;
- the severity of the condition; and
- the impact of the condition on the individual and his/her ability to carry out the ordinary activities of daily living.

For example, a child's squint is neither a particularly severe condition nor one which is likely to have a significant impact on the life of the child. Nevertheless, the long-term implications, if it is not treated by an orthoptist, could well be far-reaching from both a clinical and a financial point of view. Even so, assessing the consequences, severity and impact of a condition will be problematic and the 'personhood' as well as the 'best interest' of the individual must always be taken into account.

Consequently, certain important questions have to be asked in order to determine the need for intervention by those with appropriate expertise. First, what percentage of the population is already receiving treatment or care for a particular condition? Second, what is the nature and magnitude of both the benefit and the risk from the intervention? Last, what is the cost per case? With respect to the last two questions, not only do they involve the making of difficult judgements they also involve a choice between, on the one hand, the needs and 'best interest' of the individual and, on the other, the needs and 'best interest' of the community at large.

Clearly, to analyse every health problem in this way would be an overwhelming task. It is therefore sensible to begin with an analysis of the most common health problems. Some of the necessary information could be constructed from existing sources, such as epidemiological and screening data; clinical data held by GPs; and the results of research projects.[27] However, as many commentators point out, much of this is inaccessible and does not go far enough. For example, the Faculty of Public Health Medicine in its report, *UK Levels of Health* (1991), argues that the information regarding the health status of elderly people is particularly poor.[28] Furthermore, the General Household Survey is undertaken too infrequently and is a poor guide to the incidence and consequences of conditions, such as incontinence, immobility and poor hearing.

The attempt to define and measure need in this way not only gives rise to logistic problems but can also be subject to more profound criticism. There is a danger that, as mentioned earlier, use of existing sources of data may result in the definition and measurement of demand not need. It could also lead to the neglect of conditions which have not been established as health problems. In the past, for example, the need for the treatment of pre-menstrual tension was not recognised. Moreover, it is largely based on a biomedical approach (see Chapter 1) and therefore does not give due weight to the importance of social factors in determining need. Last, from the point of view of those seeking to operate within increasingly tight budgets, one of the principal drawbacks of need assessment is its tendency to raise expectations. In view of the scale and diversity of health care needs likely to be revealed, it will be impossible to meet them all. Thus, a number of commentators have argued that a great deal of time will have to be spent on reducing public expectations with respect to what can and will be done to meet health needs. Furthermore, professionals may have to modify their objectives in the light of reality. Indeed, Buchan and Gray go further and argue that: 'Unrestrained enthusiasm for general population need surveys may serve only to raise expectations falsely about future provision. If resources do not exist or will not be made available, the identification of needs is a futile gesture.'[29] Of course, this is unfair. Heightened expectations, even when they are not all met, can contribute in a positive way to maintaining the level and quality of services. Furthermore, by making need more explicit, the determination of priorities and the allocation of resources can be undertaken in a more systematic and democratic way. Thus, even in conditions of resource constraint the assessment of need is far from being a 'futile gesture'.

For the CHSs, the increased attention being given to need assessment is of particular relevance for two main reasons. First, because of the proactive nature of much of the health care provided in community settings, with the emphasis on prevention and education, service providers have had far greater experience in assessing need than their hospital based colleagues. Furthermore, much of the information about health needs which already exists, such as the neighbourhood and patch profiles produced by health visitors, the results of screening programmes and epidemiological data, is held by professionals based in the community. Thus, from the point of view of both the processes involved and the 'cultural climate' within which health care services are planned and delivered, they have a major contribution to make to the development of a coherent methodology for the systematic identification and assessment of health care needs. There is undoubtedly still a long way to go in this respect, but the foundations are already in place in the CHSs.

Second, a more systematic approach to the assessment of need and the consequent exposure of more of the 'iceberg' of sickness and disability will certainly strengthen still further the case for placing greater emphasis on the prevention of illness and the promotion of health. As a result, the CHSs may well benefit from the higher profile given to health care activities in which they have traditionally played a major, if not dominant, part. Moreover, a shift in emphasis of this kind, together with the increasingly complex and interrelated nature of need, may well result in a realignment of the boundaries between community health and other forms of health and social care. If this is the case, then those responsible for the CHSs, must ensure that such changes do not lead to their marginalisation within the health and social care system.

The emphasis currently being placed on need assessment has, in some respects, rejuvenated the initial stages of the traditional NHS planning process. Similarly, the move to a 'contract culture' is having a significant impact on the later stages, in particular those of **implementation and review**. Instead of plans being implemented directly by the agency responsible for their preparation they now serve as the framework for the development of a contractual relationship between planners (i.e. commissioners) and providers. In other words, there is a formal separation between the formulation and the implementation of plans. On the one hand, this can be seen as a way of sharpening up the processes involved, in that judgements and assumptions regarding needs and priorities will have to be made more explicit. On the other hand, service provision will only be as good as the contract, which in turn will depend upon the adequacy and accuracy of the need assessment. Indeed it has been argued that: '... the ability of DHAs and FHSAs to assess health needs, rather than expressed demand, for their local population, as the basis for specifying service contracts, will be a key factor in determining the sucess of the separation of commissioning organisations from providers.'[30]

For the commissioners, contracting embraces a variety of activities. First, service specifications, based on the assessment of needs and priorities and taking into account the availability of resources, must be prepared. This involves deciding:

- who should play a part in defining the service(s) covered by the specification, for example, some health authorities have consulted representatives of the lay constituency, such as the Community Health Council and voluntary organisations, as well as prospective providers;
- how services are to be classified for specification purposes; this is particularly important for the CHSs because any realignment, which may result from this, could threaten their separate identity;[31] and
- what is to be specified in the contract, with respect to inputs, care process, outputs, outcomes and delivery points.

In an attempt to deal with some of the issues surrounding questions of this kind, the NHS Management Executive produced guidance indicating that contracts can take a variety of forms (e.g. block, cost and volume, cost per case) and that measurable standards and quality specifications should also be built into contracts.[32]

Inevitably, the providers of CHSs have expressed their preferences with regard to the type of contract they are seeking. For example, in its application for trust status, one community unit indicated its preference for 'block contracts with costing based on workload dependency related sub-divisions'.[33] This type of contract was favoured on the grounds that:

- it enabled a higher percentage of expenditure (in the case of the commissioner) and of income (in the case of the provider) to be predicted in advance;
- 'unexpected increases in volume (could) be managed by agreeing in advance how (each party) should react to changes in the demand for services'; and
- 'maximum levels of provision and funding ... (could) be set allowing both parties to plan more effectively.'[34]

Clearly the preparation of good service specifications is a task of considerable complexity for all health care managers. This is particularly the case for staff working in community settings, where there is a high degree of intangibility associated with their caring, counselling, educative and promotional roles.

Second, the commissioning agency needs to identify and select suitable service providers. A variety of methods are available for this purpose, such as open tendering, select list tendering and direct negotiation with provider agencies. For CHSs, commissioners in many districts will initially be faced with a situation in which there is one major provider, with the result that the last of these methods is likely to be the most common. Clearly, where the commissioner is 'tied in' with one provider the contracting process is much simpler, but the purported benefits to be derived from the operation of market forces are significantly reduced. In particular, it becomes harder for the commissioner to secure radical changes in the pattern of service provision.

Third, performance needs to be monitored against the specification. This involves: determining which performance indicators are to be used for this purpose; producing the indicators; designating monitors; and ensuring that those responsible for the monitoring have access to everything they need. Contract compliance is clearly essential if the credibility of the dichotomy between commissioner and provider is to be maintained. Given their dispersed and disparate nature, contracts for the provision of CHSs are likely to be far more difficult to monitor than those for hospital based services.

Last, it is necessary to establish and, whenever necessary, operate procedures for the settlement of disputes, the application of penalties and the termination of contracts. Inevitably, the efficacy of some of these procedures will depend on the availability of alternative providers.

Central to all these activities is the issue of quality assurance, the importance of which has been underlined by both the proponents and opponents of a system based on contractual relationships between the commissioners and providers of health care. For example, in April 1990, the Deputy Chief Executive of the NHS stated that it would be 'a tragedy' if the first range of contracts did not include measurable statements on quality, drawn up after consultation with clinicians. Similarly, critics of the reforms, such as the BMA, have argued that with priority being given to cost-effectiveness quality will inevitably suffer.

Quality, however, is not an easy concept to apply, especially with regard to the provision of services. As Walsh comments: 'unlike material goods, (they cannot be tested) after production and before delivery.'[35] Furthermore, although quality depends, to some extent, on the skill and understanding of those directly engaged in service delivery, it is also dependent on the experiences, perceptions and expectations of the users and informal carers. Thus, their views must be obtained and incorporated in service design if high priority is being given to the pursuit of quality. 'Quality is not an absolute concept but is a matter of debate with the user or consumer'.[36]

The link between the quality of health care services and the perceptions of service users was highlighted in guidance issued to DHAs in 1990. For example, in *Developing Districts* it was made clear that in performing their commissioning role DHAs have to 'use contracts to improve the quality of services and make services more responsive to the views of users.' This means, in effect, that DHAs are expected to:

- determine 'how to assess the main quality issues';
- identify the main users of services, 'differentiating between individuals and organisations, and find out the activities which they regard as key indicators of good performance';
- ensure that the providers of health care services have 'an effective system to obtain the views of users' and that they act upon their views; and
- check that providers set 'local targets, acceptable to the DHA for improving quality whether for services generally or for one particular element.'[37]

In responding to this guidance DHAs are faced with considerable difficulties, especially with respect to community based health care services. It is no simple matter to elicit the views of geographically dispersed client groups or of those who are potential users. In addition, users may be reluctant to give their views, especially if they have been rebuffed by unsympathetic planners and providers in the past. Moreover, there is a seemingly limitless list of criteria that could be used as the basis for assessing quality and the weight attached to these will vary considerably depending upon the situation. For example, criteria which relate to comfort are likely to be given higher priority long-term recipients of a service than by others.

In attempting to overcome these difficulties a number of DHAs, such as Bloomsbury and Islington, have made use of Maxwell's six principles (i.e. equity, accessibility, appropriateness to need, efficiency, effectiveness and acceptability), as the basis of their approach. Examples of specific quality standards relating to community based services, include:

- with respect to family planning and reproductive health services 'women at all times should have access to a female doctor or nurse';

- all literature relating women's health screening services should be available in 'the major minority ethnic languages spoken in the district';
- all relevant service areas, such as clinics and health centres, 'should be easily accessible and provide facilities for babies and toddlers';
- 'the results of all screening tests should be forwarded to the client and her GP within four weeks'; and
- with respect to immunisation rates, the target should be 100% and the minimum 90%

Although formulations of this kind are of undoubted value, they can never encapsulate every aspect of quality or ensure that due attention is given to every nuance of the relationship between users and service providers. Moreover, even though attention is also being given to the establishment of mechanisms for eliciting the views of members of the lay constituency and monitoring compliance with standards derived from quality checklists, their scope will inevitably be limited. Reliance has to be placed on the integrity and expertise of service providers tempered by the availability of resources.

Despite the conceptual and practical problems associated with the issue of quality, it is likely to be one that will continue to occupy a high position on the health care agenda for many years to come. Both the major political parties are committed to improving the quality of publically provided services and therefore have a vested interest in ensuring that it is taken seriously by those with responsibility for the planning and commissioning of community and other health care services. Likewise, those in the business of service provision must, in planning their strategies, give due attention to quality, if they are to prosper.

Business Planning

Within the more commercial environment that now prevails, the principal goals of the providers of CHSs are to sell their services and thereby generate as much income as they require to remain in business. In the pursuit of these goals most providers have felt the need to prepare business plans and, in certain circumstances, undertake sophisticated marketing exercises.

Business planning has been defined by Elphick and Dillarstone as the 'process by which organisations put their mission and aims into quantified plans to be achieved over several years.'[38] In their view, the starting point for business planning is a **market assessment**. In contrast to need assessment, this involves determining:

- where existing users come from and the likely future demand for services;
- what those agencies responsible for commissioning health care services may wish to purchase;
- the market structure (i.e. monopoly, imperfect competition or perfect competition) in respect of the services concerned and the strengths and weaknesses of any competitors;
- what must be done to win contracts for the provision of services; and
- how much income is likely to be generated.

In undertaking an assessment of this kind, providers, including community units/trusts, will be obliged to make increasing use of marketing concepts and techniques. However, there is an important difference between the concept of the market as it is understood in the private sector, where the key relationship is between the provider and the customer, and the internal market where, as Davies argues, there are two key relationships. The first of these is that between the provider and the customer (i.e. the commissioner of services) and the second, that between the provider and the consumer (i.e. the user and informal carer). Therefore, the terms 'pseudo-market', 'quasi-market', 'controlled market' and 'proto-market' are often used to describe what is, in some respects, a relatively new phenomenon.

In the case of the first of the relationships described by Davies, the initial task for providers is to identify, and engage in dialogue with, potential customers. In most districts, the principal sources of business for community units/trusts are likely to be:

- DHAs (e.g. for services required by care groups, such as pre-school children, elderly persons);
- either family practitioners or the FHSA acting on their behalf (e.g. for chiropody,[39] physiotherapy and other paramedical services);
- local authority departments, such as education (e.g. for speech therapy) and social services (e.g. for occupational therapy and district nursing); and

- other organisations (e.g. for health promotion and screening facilities for employees).

In seeking to explain the nature of the relationship which is likely to develop between customers and providers, Davies suggests that the concept of relational marketing is of particular value. This is 'typified by a willingness to share data, to exchange managers, to identify costs that can be reduced only by mutual consent'.[40] In which case the two parties will 'not see each other as mutually threatening'. Instead, they will seek to work together as closely as possible. However, the danger with this kind of approach is that it may lead to the development of cartels, which will not necessarily work to the benefit of consumers.

As well as identifying, and forming close relationships with, customers, community units/trusts also have to give consideration to the likelihood of competition from other providers. Possible competitors of community units/trusts include:

- other units/trusts, in respect of clinical services which are not seen as the exclusive preserve of a particular unit (e.g. psychology, physiotherapy);
- voluntary bodies, in areas where specialist expertise is needed (e.g. terminal care); and
- private sector organisations, including those established by ex-employees, who have 'bought out' of units/trusts, in respect of profitable services (e.g. chiropody, home nursing).

In reality, the market position facing community units/trusts will vary from district to district and inevitably this will affect their marketing strategy. For example, where there are a number of providers, some will seek a modest share of a large market (e.g. for district nursing services) and others a substantial share of a smaller, specialist market (e.g. for dietetics).

Turning to the second relationship, namely that between the provider and the consumer, Davies argues that the most appropriate concept is that of services marketing, which involves paying particular attention to the expectations of users and informal carers with respect to quality. Unconstrained by considerations of price these are likely to be high. Consequently, 'managing expectations is ... an important aspect of services marketing'.[41]

Arguably, the extent to which services marketing techniques are used will depend on the intensity of the competition facing providers. For example, where there is a great deal of competition, providers will have to pay particular attention to the views of consumers and ensure that the quality of the service provided meets or exceeds their expectations.

At the same time as undertaking a market assessment, it is usual to produce a **mission statement** or statement of purpose. This is essentially an attempt to answer the question: Why are we here? or What are we in business for? As the mission statements produced by community units/trusts illustrate (see Figure 5.2 for some examples), they usually refer to the philosophy and values which underpin the unit's/trust's operations. They can also be said to reflect the expectations of clinicians, managers, users, informal carers, voluntary organisations, the government and other constituencies.

Extracts from Mission Statements Produced by Units and Trusts with Responsibility for Community Health Services

Anglian Harbours Health Trust

'... to promote positive health and well being through a caring and informed service which will be provided in the community, on a domiciliary basis and in a range of local hospitals'

Cornwall Community Services Trust

'... to promote good health in the community whilst providing local care to those in need'

Croydon Community Health Trust

'... to provide good quality, well co-ordinated, locally sensitive, primary and continuing care in partnership with GPs and others.'

To meet this statement of purpose the trust has 'developed five key philosophies for (its) services, management styles and information and monitoring systems.' These are:

- *targetting need,*
- *patient choice,*
- *care group planning,*
- *neighbourhood provision and*
- *prevention.*

The First Community Health Trust (Mid Staffs)

'... all our efforts will be aimed at providing a high quality service which is comprehensive, efficient and 'customer friendly''

North West Herts Priority Health Services Trust

'... the Trust is in the business of enabling people to develop or regain self dependence and to provide long term assistance that prolongs independence'

Rotherham Priority Services Unit

'... to provide ever improving comprehensive, high quality services to the people of Rotherham and other consumers, which maximise the physical, psychological and social well being of individuals and their carers, enabling them to live as independent and full a life as possible.'

Figure 5.2

According to the advocates of business planning, the importance of the mission statement lies in the fact that, without a vision and sense of direction based on explicit values, health care providers might well founder in the market place. In other words, they must have a clear view of the strategic direction of their business in order to survive and, hopefully, prosper.

Thus, once it has been produced, a mission statement serves as the basis for the development of a strategy. This addresses the question: What is to be done? It usually consists of a set of broad aims expressed in terms of:

- specific services (e.g. to establish and operate a system of child health surveillance which will allow preventable or treatable conditions to be detected as early as possible);
- management practices (e.g. to reward staff more flexibly in line with the need to attract and retain them and encourage good innovative practice); and
- management processes (e.g. to develop in liaison with the community, locally provided services which are responsive to the needs of users).

The next step is to convert these essentially qualititative aims into a more concrete business plan. This indicates how the aims are to be achieved and, most importantly, the resources that must be committed. It generally covers the volume, quality and cost of activities and identifies priorities and key tasks. In addition, the plan should specify the mechanisms for the monitoring and review of performance. Examples of mechanisms being used or planned by community units/trusts include:

- local advisory groups;
- individual patient feedback from letters of complaint and of thanks;
- surveys;
- medical audit; and
- service/quality flow charts.

Given the attention which commissioners are required to give to quality assurance, it is clearly essential for providers to do the same. Put simply, if they fail to respond positively to pressure for improvements in the quality of services, they risk losing contracts. Of course, commissioning agencies may not exert such pressure because of the financial constraints which they face and the imperative to stay within budget.

Finally, business plans provide a framework within which timed targets can be set; resource constraints specified; and responsibility for achievement can be assigned to named individuals. This can then be integrated with staff appraisal systems and with mechanisms for financial management and control. Of particular importance in this respect are developments in the sphere of resource management which are designed to enable managers to answer the questions: How much service is being provided? To whom? At what cost? In the words of Deffenbaugh: 'Once the plan is drafted, implementation then presents the real challenge.'[42]

One of the consequences of the move towards business planning is the strengthening of the managerial vis-a-vis the clinical constituency. This is even more marked within trusts, where there is greater freedom to determine pay and conditions on the basis of the situation in local labour markets.

All providers, whether having trust status or not, will be seeking to offer services to prospective commissioners at a competitive price. For the CHSs pricing has proved to be particularly difficult due to the problems involved in identifying and defining the 'health product'. Nonetheless, progress is being made in various parts of country. For example, in North Derbyshire managers have developed the concept of 'programmes of health care' as a means of classifying CHSs; determining the information necessary to support these services; and devising a method of costing them. In other words, 'programmes of health care' can be seen as a community equivalent of 'diagnostic related groups'.[43]

It is important not to see the production of business plans as a once and for all, or even a periodic, activity. It is a continuous process and one which needs a high level of commitment on the part of all those involved. Moreover, it requires both managers and clinicians to be flexible so that opportunities can be exploited as soon as they arise and speedy action can be taken to deal with any threats.

Some would argue that the very survival of providers of CHSs in a more commercial environment depends, to some extent, upon the successful application of the precepts of business planning. Although there is undoubtedly some truth in this, the situation is complicated by the fact that the future of the CHSs is very much bound up with attempts to secure a more integrated approach to the planning of primary and community care and to ensure that the values of the 'contract culture' operate throughout the health and social care system.

Integrated Planning

Traditionally one of the weakest aspects of health care planning has been in respect of what could be described as horizontal integration. From the point of view of community health care, this means ensuring that plans for the CHSs are compatible with those for HSs, FHSs and personal social services. The reasons for this state of affairs are well documented[44] and they suggest that progress in this sphere is, at best, likely to be painfully slow. An additional complication is that planning for the voluntary sector can no longer be regarded as a totally separate enterprise.

Nevertheless, strenuous efforts are being made to secure a more integrated and coherent approach to the planning of community health and family health services (i.e. primary care) and community health and social services (i.e. community care). Because of their pivotal position within the health and social care system, those committed to the CHSs, whether as employees of commissioning authorities or of provider organisations, clearly have a key role to play in this respect. However, in assisting with the development of an integrated approach to planning, they may (albeit unwittingly) contribute to the loss of a separate identity for the CHSs. This is not necessarily a bad thing. If it is done in an overt and informed way, it may help to counter the ill effects of the fragmentation endemic in the health and social care system. The danger is that this will not be the case and the distinctive contributions of CHSs staff will be eroded by stealth. In this respect, it is worrying that the CHSs are scarcely mentioned in the primary health care strategy documents of some RHAs.[45]

With regard to **primary care planning**, Marks makes the point that this 'has long represented a policy void, partly as a result of (the) fragmentation of services, and partly due to the independent contractor status of those providing family practitioner (now health) services.'[46] Attempts to remedy this situation have been gathering pace since the mid 1980s.

First, in 1982 the government indicated its intention to reconstitute FPCs as 'independent' employing authorities in their own right, in the hope that this would result in a 'closer working partnership' between DHAs and FPCs 'to serve the interests of the community, especially in relation to primary health care'. A year later the government set up the Joint Working Group on Collaboration between Family Practitioner Committees and District Health Authorities. This was given the following terms of reference:

> *To identify the aims and principles of collaboration between ... DHAs and ... FPCs, and formal and informal measures for securing them; the contribution which FPCs should make to health services planning; and the scope for exchange of appropriate information between DHAs and FPCs for that and other purposes.*

The recommendations of the Working Group (1984) incorporated a set of precepts for successful collaboration as well as some practical proposals relating to the planning system and to areas of joint concern, such as dentistry, community nursing, community medicine and health promotion.[47] In this way the Group helped to set the tone and agenda for DHA-FPC relations in the period immediately after 1985, when FPCs eventually secured their 'independence'.

Second, during the second half of the 1980s, a number of projects and studies to determine how best to facilitate a joint approach to service development and delivery, were sponsored by the DHSS and other bodies. These included:

- the East London collaboration project, which focussed on primary dental services;
- the Liverpool collaboration project, which was concerned with the whole range of primary care services delivered to a particular community (i.e. Speke estate); and
- the Halton and Loughborough studies, which examined the co-ordination, planning and delivery of primary care.

Each of these projects/studies demonstrated the scope for collaboration, but illustrated the high level of commitment needed to realise its full potential.

Third, DHSS/DH planning guidelines issued to FPCs and DHAs in the second half of the 1980s indicated that they should give priority to collaboration. In order to reinforce the guidelines, consideration was given to the progress being made in applying them at the annual meetings held to review the performance of individual authorities.

Fourth, in the white paper, *Promoting Better Health* (1987), recognition was given to the progress which had been made in respect of cervical cancer screening and other areas of mutual concern. However, it was acknowledged that more needed to be done and the government spelt out its commitment to 'effective collaboration in ... areas where it remain(ed) weak'.[48]

Fifth, on 1st April 1990 FPCs were reconstituted as FHSAs and they were made accountable to RHAs instead of directly to the DH. This was intended to signal 'a reduction in the isolation of FHSAs ... from other local health services'.[49] Following the change, RHAs have required 'FHSAs to develop much closer relationships with DHAs' and have been issuing joint planning guidelines to facilitate moves towards the production of joint strategies and plans reflecting jointly agreed priorities.

Sixth, in accordance with the provisions of the National Health Service and Community Care Act 1990, FHSAs and DHAs are now required to share responsibility for assessing the health needs of their populations. In addition, documents emanating from initiatives taken by the NHS Management Executive have drawn attention to the need for so-called 'healthy alliances' between FHSAs and DHAs; to the potential for the joint commissioning of services; and to the importance of developing '**joint** rather than separate health profiles of their local populations'.[50] Moreover, in looking ahead, the NHS Management Executive's paper, *Family Health Services Authorities Today's and Tomorrow's Priorities* (1991), suggested a number of alternative models on which the future relationship between FHSAs and DHAs might be based. These are:

- 'a dynamic status quo model which builds on the strengths of the existing DHA/FHSA arrangement ...;
- a model which emphasises the provider role of the FHSA and the links it might develop ...;
- a model which concentrates on the integration of purchasing arrangements, with the FHSA's commissioning role emphasised ...; and
- a primary health care authority model which unites family health and community health services, integrating commissioning and provision ...'

Significantly, in various parts of the country joint commissioning is now becoming more of a reality.

Last, there have been some important developments in the sphere of community nursing, which is one of the key components of primary care. Community nursing embraces such services as those provided by district nurses, health visitors and community midwives employed by

DHAs and trusts and those provided by nurses employed by GPs. Arguably, the most significant of the developments has been the substantial increase in the number of GP practice nurses. Even though this might contribute to a more integrated approach to the planning and delivery of care, it has generated a considerable amount of controversy. In resourcing this expansion the government has clearly demonstrated its rejection of one of the key Cumberlege recommendations namely that: 'Subsidies to general practitioners enabling them to employ staff to perform nursing duties should be phased out'.[51] In so doing, it has undermined a philosophy of primary care based on the neighbourhood nursing team; the autonomous nurse practitioner; and the central position of DHAs and community units/trusts with respect to the planning and organisation of community nursing services. In its stead, it offers a community nursing service subordinate to general practice. This will inevitably result in a more biomedical approach to nursing in community settings and less accountability to the public because of the nature of the GPs' contractual relationship with the NHS. Moreover, the situation is complicated by the issue of gender inequality. A major shift in the distribution of community nurses from DHAs/trusts to general practice, will undoubtedly hinder efforts to secure a more collaborative approach to the planning of primary health care.

In recognition of the problems arising from existing divisions within community nursing, the centre has felt it necessary to ensure that the expansion of the practice nurse labour force 'be co-ordinated with DHA plans for community nursing services'. For this reason the NHS Management Executive commissioned a working party 'to consider the broad management principles which authorities and practitioners should apply to ensure that any changes or realignment of services be effectively managed.'[52]

In its report the working party identified the following principles as underpinning more effectively managed services and being of equal relevance to commissioners and providers:

- a shared vision of care;
- a commitment to joint working and putting patients first;
- joint assessment of population health needs;
- joint strategies;
- effective communications; and

- a commitment to quality.[53]

The working party also gave consideration to possible future organisational and management arrangements for community nursing services and summarised their findings in a series of models. These are:

- the 'stand-alone' community trust or directly managed unit (DMU);
- locality management/neighbourhood nursing;
- the expanded FHSA;
- vertical integration or outreach model; and
- the GP managed primary health care team model.[54]

It is still too early to know what the future holds for community nursing, but it is possible that a so-called 'mixed economy' pattern may emerge. In essence, this would mean competition between a variety of providers (i.e. DMUs, trusts, voluntary organisations, nursing agencies, GP practice nurse teams) for community nursing contracts let by FHSAs/DHAs and local authorities.

Despite the long-standing uncertainty and controversy surrounding aspects of primary care planning, it is accepted by many that FHSs should be more closely integrated with CHSs in the interests of securing improvements in the quality and cost-effectiveness of care. Indeed, it can be argued that, in view of the nature of many of the components of the 'crisis in health' (see Chapter 1), the relationship between GPs (and other family practitioners) and the CHSs will be of greater consequence in the future, than that between GPs and HSs. Many fear, however, that a higher profile for community based health care will mean the further strengthening of the position of general practice at the expense of the CHSs (see Chapter 7 for a discussion of the dangers inherent in a development of this kind).

Although initiatives designed to facilitate **community care planning** predate those taken in respect of the planning of primary care services, on the whole this head-start has not made much difference to the current situation. At one time it was hoped that the joint planning machinery and joint financing arrangements established after the reorganisations of the NHS and local government in 1974 would provide a suitably robust framework within which to develop a collaborative approach to the preparation of plans for community health and social care services. However, they failed to fulfil these initial expectations. Even the government's verdict on joint planning, as expressed in *Caring* *for People*, was that: 'The record ... has been mixed. A modest success can be claimed if judged against realistic criteria but it nevertheless falls short of the aspirations of the mid-1970s.'[55]

In seeking to deal with the shortcomings of the past, the government has assigned to social services authorities a role in respect of community care which is very similar to that of DHAs in respect of health care. They are required to prepare community care plans containing, amongst other things, an assessment of the needs of the population they serve; their strategic objectives for community care in the next three years and how these relate to national policy objectives; details of how they intend to identify and meet their needs for information on which to base planning; and the arrangements for assessing individual applicants for care.[56] Moreover, they will be responsible for commissioning services to meet the community care needs of their population, including those with a health component, and for concluding contracts or service agreements with a wide range of providers. Thus, inherent in these reforms is the concept of the 'enabling authority' commissioning services from 'arms length' providers and monitoring standards.

Not surprisingly, under the planning regime enunciated in *Caring for People* collaboration also receives a great deal of attention. First, social services authorities are expected to indicate in their community care plans how they intend to co-ordinate their 'activities with those of health authorities, family practitioner committees (now FHSAs) and housing authorities'.[57] Second, health authorities must decide whether their community care plans 'would best form part of their overall plans or should be produced separately as a joint exercise with the relevant local authorities.' However, whatever is decided, the 'key contents and resource assumptions (of these plans) will need to be shared and agreed with the social services authority.' Last, and most importantly, it is intended 'to base future public policy on planning agreements ... encompass(ing) a realistic range of key requirements to be reflected in both health and local authority plans.' These requirements are:

- 'common goals derived at least partly from national policy aims for particular client groups';
- 'funding agreements, setting out the basis on which health and social care will be funded';
- 'agreed policies on key operational areas, such as quality standards, assessment policies and procedures and discharge policies'; and

- 'agreed contract specifications for securing joint working between service providers.'[58]

However, despite the attention given to collaboration, little has been done to clarify the boundary between health care and social care. Thus, it remains to be seen whether the rhetoric can be successfully converted into reality. Past experience suggests that, unless the benefits to the participants outweigh the costs, progress will, at best, continue to be slow. Nevertheless, there are grounds for believing that market forces may succeed in this respect where other devices have failed. This is because the information requirements involved in the introduction of a market relationship may make some of the benefits and costs more visible, concrete and direct.

Given the profound changes in the nature of planning and associated developments considered in this chapter and the political controversy surrounding them, it is impossible to predict with any degree of certainty what the eventual outcome will be for the CHSs. It is possible, however, to identify a number of factors that are likely to play a part in shaping the way in which CHSs are planned. These include:

- a commitment to the more explicit assessment of health care needs;
- the preparation of service specifications;
- a concern with issues of quality;
- a clear distinction between the roles of commissioner of services and of provider;
- increasing collaboration between commissioners;
- competition between providers; and
- greater flexibility in the use of staff which, given that this is the most expensive resource, may result in the replacement of qualified professionals with less well qualified employees, especially at the point of service delivery.

Under different governments the vocabulary may change and the interpretation of these factors may differ. Nevertheless, whatever happens on the broader political front, the 'crisis in health' and the lessons of the past will ensure that factors of this kind influence the climate within which the planning and delivery of community based health services takes place.

Notes

1 For further details, see R. Ottewill and A. Wall, *The Growth and Development of the Community Health Services* (Sunderland: Business Education Publishers, 1990), pp.94-5.

2 Ibid., pp.201-4 and 211.

3 Ibid., pp.201-3, 301-6 and 318.

4 For further details, see DH, Health Circular HC(88)64, *Health Services Management. Health of the Population: Responsibilities of Health Authorities*, December 1988, and ibid., pp.373-5.

5 Section 46 of the National Health Service and Community Care Act 1990 states that 'Each local authority shall... prepare and publish a plan for the provision of community care services in their area'. In carrying out this function, 'a local authority shall consult any (DHA) the whole or any part of whose district lies within the area of the local authority... (and) any (FHSA) the whole or any part of whose locality lies within the area of the local authority'.

6 As indicated in Chapter 4, the publication of *The Health of the Nation* in 1991 placed the setting of targets firmly on the health care agenda. For further discussion of the contents and significance of this document, see Chapters 6 and 7.

7 For a more detailed analysis of the development of different approaches to planning within the NHS, see J. Edmonstone and M. Havergal, 'Business Planning: new wine in old bottles?', *Health Services Management*, February 1991, pp.33-35. They identify four approaches: investment planning, normative planning, performance planning and competitive planning.

8 Ibid., p.34.

9 Throughout this chapter the term 'commissioning' is used rather than 'purchasing' since it is less politically charged. Moreover, underlying the term 'commissioning' is the belief that services should not be provider-led. In other words, the agencies responsible for assessing health care needs and securing services to meet them should have the final say in determining which services are provided. For a fuller discussion of the commissioning role, see, for example, Barking and Havering FHSA and Barking, Havering and Brentwood HA, *Commissioning of Primary and Community Health Services 1992* (Romford: Barking and Havering FHSA, 1992).

10 See, for example, A. McNaught (ed.), *Managing Community Health Services* (London: Chapman and Hall, 1991), esp. pp.23-4 and 84.

11 For details of agencies and professional groups, see R. Ottewill and A. Wall, op.cit., esp. ch.8.

12 D. Hunter, 'Planning Ahead for 1991', *The Health Service Journal*, 22 March 1990, p.442.

13 P. Kemp, 'No stalling for the NHS internal market', *Public Finance and Accountancy*, 15 June 1990, p.13-17.

14 L. Marks (ed.), *Planning Primary Care* (London: King's Fund Centre, 1989), p.7.

15 P. Kemp, op.cit.

16 The Open University, *Managing Health Services. Book 2 Decision Making and Planning* (Milton Keynes, The Open University: 1990), p.13.

17 DH, Circular HC(88)64, op.cit.

18 National Health Service Review, Working Paper 1, *Self Governing Hospitals* (London: HMSO, 1989), para.3.2.

19 R. Titmuss, *Essays on the Welfare State*, Second Edition (London: Unwin University Books, 1969), p.39.

20 NHS Management Executive, *FHSAs - Today's and Tomorrow's Priorities*, January 1991, p.12.

21 P. Charlwood, 'Figuring out the finance of the NHS reforms', *Public Finance and Accountancy*, 2 November 1990, pp.11-13.

22 F. Eskin and A. Bull, 'Squaring a Difficult Circle', *The Health Service Journal*, 10 January 1991, pp.16-19.

23 For example, in *The Health Report 1990* produced by North East Thames Regional Health Authority the point is made that: 'In drawing up contracts for services, purchasing (commissioning) authorities should know the health and service needs of ethnic groups. Contractual arrangements should incorporate these needs' (p.14).

24 See Health Education Authority, *NHS White Paper : Implications for Health Promotion/Disease Prevention* (Health Education Authority: London, 1990), for a discussion of the special characteristics of the assessment of need for health promotion and disease prevention services.

25 Department of Health, Chief Medical Officer's Professional Letter, PL/CMO(90)12, *Annual Health Reports of Directors of Public Health*, 7 December 1990, para.2.

26 H. Buchan, M. Gray et.al., 'Needs Assessment Made Simple', *The Health Service Journal*, 15 February 1990, pp.240-1.

27 Ibid.

28 The Faculty of Public Health Medicine of the Royal Colleges of Medicine, *UK Levels of Health: First Report* (London: The Faculty of Public Health Medicine, 1991).

29 H. Buchan, M. Gray et.al., op.cit. See also G. Davies, 'Picking a philosophy', *The Health Service Journal*, 7 March 1991, pp.20-1.

30 J. Bromley, et.al., *Developing FHSAs*, undated, para. 3.1.

31 Bloomsbury and Islington Health Authority, for example, have prepared specifications for groups of services, many of which cut across the traditional boundaries between community and other forms of health care. These include:

services for children and adolescents;
family planning and reproductive health services;
women's health screening services;
services for people with learning difficulties;
mental health services;
community and hospital dental services;
HIV/AIDS services;
services for people with physical disabilities; and
services for older people.

32 In *Self Governing Hospitals: An initial guide* (London: HMSO, 1989), the different kinds of contract are defined in the following terms:

block contracts, the purchaser pays the provider 'an annual fee, in instalments, in return for access to a defined range and level of services';

cost and volume contracts, the provider receives 'a fixed sum for a baseline level of activity, defined in terms of a given number of treatments or cases ... beyond that level, cases (are) funded on a cost per case basis'; and

cost per case contracts, the purchaser pays the provider a negotiated sum per case.

33 This means, in effect, that in assessing the costs of treatment account should be taken of the fact that the condition of patients will mean that they require varying amounts of a service provider's time.

34 Croydon Community Health Trust, *Trust Application*, June 1990, para.2.3.

35 K. Walsh, *Marketing in Local Government* (Harlow: Longman, 1989), p.7.

36 Ibid., p.8.

37 DH, *Working for Patients: Developing Districts* (London: HMSO, 1990), para. 2.11.

38 C. Elphick and P. Dillarstone, 'Order out of Chaos', *The Health Service Journal*, 8 February 1990, p.200.

39 For details of an arrangement in Wakefield whereby the community and priority unit has entered into a contract with the FHSA for the provision of chiropody services at GP premises, see A. Hopkins, 'Putting a foot right', *The Health Service Journal*, 28 March 1991, p.23.

40 G. Davies, op.cit.

41 Ibid.

42 J. Deffenbaugh, 'Debunking the plans bunkum', *The Health Service Journal*, 16 May 1991, p.23.

43. For further details of the approach adopted by North Derbyshire, see C. Fretwell, S. A. Vidall and W. Dale, 'The right system at the right time', *The Health Service Journal*, 2 May 1991, pp.16-18.

44. See, for example, the report of the Working Group on Joint Planning, *Progress in Partnership* (London: HMSO, 1985); the report of The House of Commons Social Services Committee, *Community Care, with special reference to adult mentally ill and mentally handicapped people*, House of Commons Paper No.13, Session 1984-85; the Audit Commission report, *Making a Reality of Community Care* (London: HMSO, 1986), in which the arrangements for joint planning were described as being 'in some disarray', p.3; and G. Warren and J. Harrow, 'Working with local authorities' in A. McNaught (ed.), op.cit.

45 For example, there is a failure to recognise the significance of the contribution made by the CHSs in a Report of the Primary Health Care Strategy Group (established by North East Thames RHA), *Primary Health Care in the 90s - A strategic statement* (1991).

46 L. Marks (ed.), op.cit., p.6.

47 For further details, see R. Ottewill and A. Wall, op.cit., pp.376-7.

48 DHSS, *Promoting Better Health: The Government's Programme for Improving Primary Health Care*, Cm 249 (London: HMSO, 1987), para.10.3.

49 *FHSAs - Today's and Tomorrow's Priorities*, op.cit., p.8.

50 NHS Management Executive, *Integrating Primary and Secondary Care*, February 1991, paras.30 and 33.

51 DHSS, *Neighbourhood Nursing A Focus for Care*, [the Cumberlege Report](London: HMSO, 1986), pp.62-64.

52 North West Thames RHA, *Nursing in the Community*, December 1990, p.2.

53 Ibid., pp.7-10.

54 Ibid.

55 DH, *Caring for People – community care in the next decade and beyond*, CM 849 (London: HMSO, 1989), para.6.9.

56 Ibid., para.5.6.

57 Ibid., para.5.10.

58 Ibid., para.6.10.

CHAPTER 6

Public Health

Due, in part, to the 'crisis in health' (see Chapter 1), there has been, in recent years, a reawakening of interest in public health, both as a concept and as an activity. This can be seen in the burgeoning literature on the subject[1] and in the emergence of the so-called 'new' public health movement comprising academics, practitioners, pressure groups, voluntary organisations, local authorities and other agencies.[2]

Public health derives its *raison d'etre* from the recognition that the promotion and maintenance of health depends upon the possession of certain basic social resources. These are spelt out in the charter for public health produced by the Public Health Alliance (see Figure 6.1).

As pointed out in Chapter 2, the two key constituencies which regulate the production and distribution of these essential resources are government and business and industry, of which the latter are sometimes overlooked in the analysis of health and health care. Yet, in reality, their actions have a greater impact on the health of the nation than those of the formal health care system. Many hope that growing recognition of the significance for health of public policy initiatives and the behaviour of companies will lead to a 'major renaissance in public health both within and beyond the NHS'.[3] The consequences of this for the CHSs could be far-reaching since many in the 'new' public health movement believe that the formal health care system should be reoriented to give pride of place to community based services.

The Charter for Public Health

The following are the essential base of every citizen's right to good health:

INCOME
which provides the material means to remain healthy

HOMES
that are safe, warm, dry, secure and affordable

FOOD
that is safe, nourishing, widely available and cheap

TRANSPORT
that permits accessible, safe travel at reasonable cost and encourages fuel economy and a clean environment

WORK
properly rewarded, in or out of the home, which is worthwhile and free from hazards to health and safety

ENVIRONMENTS
protected from dangerous pollution and radiation, and planned to preserve and enhance our quality of life

PUBLIC SERVICES
which provide care for those who need it, and support for carers; clean, safe water and waste disposal; adequate childcare and recreation facilities

EDUCATION AND HEALTH PROMOTION
which give all the necessary information to keep us healthy, and the confidence and resources to tackle the causes of ill health

COMPREHENSIVE HEALTH SERVICES
properly resourced, free at the point of use and sensitive to our health needs

EQUAL OPPORTUNITY
to good health regardless of class, race, sex, physical ability, age or sexual orientation

Figure 6.1

In the past, there has often been a close, even symbiotic, relationship between public health and community health care. In part this was due to the fact that, until 1974, there was a strong organisational link between the two, since the CHSs were organised and managed as part of the public health remit of the local authority based medical officers of health (MOsH). However, other considerations also need to be taken into account. First, a public health approach reflects an acceptance of a broader view of the determinants of health, encompassing socio-economic and environmental, as well as biological, factors, a view long held by some of the health care professionals working in community settings. Second, the practice of public health requires effective collaboration across a broad spectrum of health care interests, including community health care. Third, some of the values inherent in a public health approach, such as equality, proaction, self-determination and community participation, have a particular significance for the CHSs, with their bias towards the promotion of health, prevention of ill health and support for vulnerable groups in non-institutional settings.

Consequently, any enhancement of the status of public health could lead to a strengthening of the position of the CHSs and more favourable conditions within which to apply the insights of the social approach to health (see Chapter 1). If progress is to be made towards the realisation of the WHO's public health objective of 'an acceptable state of health for all by the year 2000', effective collaboration with the CHSs is essential. Indeed, new opportunities for cooperation between CHSs staff and those active in the fields of public and environmental health are being opened up. During the past few years many intersectoral networks and groups with a HFA, healthy cities, or public health remit have been established in different parts of the country.[4]

A public health approach, highlighting the importance of work done in community settings, is also being built into an increasing number of education programmes for health professionals, most notably nurses through Project 2000. Moreover, in reassessing their role, some town planners are pleading 'for the reinstatement of health - good health for all the people - as a major goal of planning'.[5] They are also claiming that 'public investment, ... local authority powers (and) funds for projects which help people shape their own environments' are essential prerequisites for the planning of healthy cities.[6]

Given the impact which a revival of public health could have on community health care, some of the issues arising from this development and their relevance for the CHSs are discussed in this chapter. In the sections which follow consideration is given to:

- the nature of public health and the reasons for the emergence of the 'new' public health movement;
- to four practical expressions of the 'new' public health, namely the implementation of the main recommendations of the Acheson Committee of Inquiry into the Future Development of the Public Health Function (1988);[7] the strategy for the 1990s set out in *The Nation's Health,* which was produced by an independent, prestigious, multidisciplinary committee (1988);[8] the HFA targets approved by the WHO's Regional Committee for Europe (1984);[9] and the green paper *The Health of the Nation* (1991);[10] and
- the implications of applying some of the insights of the 'new' public health to the CHSs.

In so doing, attention will be drawn to some of the areas illustrated in Figure 1.1, where there is a 'community of interest' between CHSs staff and those committed to the cause of public health.

The Nature of Public Health

The precise meaning of the expression 'public health' is somewhat elusive. In the past, many definitions were relatively narrow, with the term being associated primarily with sanitary hygiene and epidemic disease control. Moreover, a distinction was often drawn between public health, meaning a concern with actions designed to maintain and improve the health of the population at large, and personal health services, of which the CHSs were a significant component, which were 'provided for the good of the citizen in need of individual care and attention'.[11] More recent definitions, however, have tended to be far broader and encompass social resources as well as most forms of health care, including that provided by CHSs staff. Acheson and his colleagues, for example, adopted such a definition, based on that formulated by the WHO in 1952, namely 'the science and art of preventing disease, prolonging life and promoting health through organised efforts of society.'[12] Similarly, the authors of *The Nation's Health* opted for the following all-embracing definition: 'the promotion of health, the prevention of disease, the treatment of illness, the care of those who are disabled and the continuous development of the technical and social means for the pursuit of these objectives.'[13] Clearly, such definitions subsume community health care.

Nevertheless, it would be an oversimplification to equate narrow definitions with the 'old' public health and broad definitions with the 'new'. The situation is far more complex, since account also needs to be taken of attitudes towards the biomedical and social approaches and towards the curative and preventive approaches to health care; of the relative importance attached to lifestyle and to socio-environmental factors; and of the positions taken in relation to the concepts of 'personhood' and 'best interest' (see Chapter 2). These are connected with the changing power relations amongst professional groups, between professionals and the lay constituency and between central and local agencies.

One of the most controversial aspects of the debate surrounding the nature of public health concerns the extent to which individuals should be held responsible for their own health and the role which government should play in the health arena. This was highlighted by Robert Maxwell, the Secretary to the King's Fund, in the preface to *The Nation's Health*. He described as 'sterile' the argument between those who maintained that 'people's health is in their own hands, dependent on their own behaviour (and) those who (took) a determinist position.' For determinists, the government could not stand aloof from the health care arena since 'through legislation, economic policy, taxation' and other means it helped to shape the choices which individuals made. According to Maxwell, both these views were correct, 'there is much for individuals to do, and much that depends on government action, and the two are frequently interdependent and interacting.'[14] Although this is undoubtedly true, many commentators have felt the need to reaffirm the case for government intervention in the light of the shift from collectivism, associated with government policy, since the mid 1970s.[15]

The 'Old' Public Health

As McKeown points out, in the nineteenth century public health was 'preventive in outlook and emphasised improvements in the environment as a means of promoting health.'[16] It was also collectivist and proactive in its orientation, with a strong emphasis on policy formulation by experts to secure the 'greatest good of the greatest number'. Underlying this was the belief that some goods and services such as utilities like water should be regulated to ensure adherence to health related standards.

At national level the principal roles were played by key individuals like Edwin Chadwick and John Simon[17] and at local level by MOsH employed by local authorities. Significantly, Chadwick had served as private secretary to Bentham the leading exponent of utilitarianism (see Chapter 2). The necessary political support for such an approach was forthcoming because of the inability of privileged residents of urban areas, who were usually opposed to collective action because of its impact on the level of local taxation, to insulate themselves from the successive waves of cholera experienced by their poorer neighbours.[18] Thus, the public health movement of the nineteenth century was an admixture of benevolent despotism, ratepayers' self-interest and social control, instigated for, rather than by, the mass of the people, who were treated as a homogenous group.

Even though this approach to public health made a significant contribution to the health of the population at large, most commentators agree that it failed to maintain its emphasis on social resources for health and it did not prove to be sufficiently flexible or robust to cope with subsequent developments in health care. There are, however, disagreements concerning the chronology of its demise.

Ashton and Seymour, for example, argue that the 'old' public health only 'lasted until the 1870s and was in time eclipsed by a more individualistic approach ushered in by the development of the germ theory of disease and the possibilities offered by immunization and vaccination'.[19] Lewis makes a similar point although she dates the decline of the 'old' public health to the inter-war period. In her view public health 'lost its way' because of its failure to develop a sound theoretical base at a time when the biomedical model and associated curative approach to health care were gaining in credibility. Thus, the increasing commitment on the part of MOsH to the development of personal health care services caused them to neglect 'many aspects of their duties as community watchdogs during the 1930s in respect both to more traditional areas such as immunization and to the new found concerns over the effects of long-term unemployment on nutritional standards and levels of morbidity and mortality'.[20] In other words, MOsH, who had been custodians of, and pivotal stakeholders in, the 'old' public health, were seduced by the attractions of those personal services, which were to become the nucleus of community health care, and lost the vision of their nineteenth century predecessors. Some commentators, however, argue that the inter-war years witnessed a revival of interest in social resources for health. For example, the establishment of the Ministry of Health in 1919 with a remit for public housing, as well as health, signalled a 'massive intervention by the state into the housing market, such that nearly 40% of all new houses were state-built. There was seen to be as clear a correlation between overcrowding and infant mortality in the twentieth century as between poor sanitation and cholera in the nineteenth.'[21]

With the creation of the NHS, however, health policy was increasingly equated with the provision of clinically based, personal health services. This was symbolised by the gradual marginalisalisation of MOsH by the powerful medical hierarchy, which was committed to a biomedical model and a curative approach to health care. In other words, MOsH failed to secure for themselves a central role in the newly created NHS. Thus, in *Changing the Public Health*, it is suggested that 'the demise of the concept of public health in the tradition of Chadwick began with the establishment of the National Health Service and was finalized with the elimination of the post of medical officer of health in 1974.'[22]

Turning to the relationship between the 'old' public health and community health care, several points are worthy of note. First, many of the community based personal health services which MOsH helped to establish in the early twentieth century (e.g. those for mothers and children) drew their inspiration from public health initiatives taken in the nineteenth century with respect to their preventive and proactive orientation. Second, as indicated earlier, during the first half of the twentieth century there was a 'changing emphasis in public health from the societal to the individual'[23] and from a concern with the wider social determinants of health to the provision of services. Although some see this as a retrograde step, from the point of view of the CHSs it had a number of desirable consequences and it ensured that they received, at a critical stage in their development, much needed attention. Furthermore, there is no reason why a concern for personal health should automatically mean that action on behalf of the population at large should be neglected. Third, during the inter-war period, it was hoped that in exercising administrative responsibility for both curative and preventive services MOsH would be in a good position to secure their integration. Of particular importance in this respect was the fact that the CHSs were able to incorporate aspects of the curative approach to health care (e.g. home nursing) while retaining a strong preventive element (e.g. health visiting), thereby demonstrating that the curative and the preventive were complementary rather than mutually exclusive. Last, even after 1948, since they retained responsibility for the CHSs as well as environmental health services, MOsH had the potential, at least, to develop a broader approach to public health, by blending the emphasis on the environmental causes of disease from the nineteenth century with the emphasis on personal health from the twentieth century. Unfortunately, however, many MOsH lacked the will, political backing and resources to transform public health in this way.

With the reorganisations of the NHS and local government in 1974, there were hopes that public health would be revitalised through the discipline of community medicine. In the event this did not happen, for reasons which are discussed in Ottewill and Wall,[24] and public health remained in the doldrums for a number of years. Moreover, as a number of commentators have pointed out, the 'new integrated health service represented a further medicalisation of public health' since it was now 'located within a health service primarily concerned with care and the delivery of services which were designed to cure patients'.[25] The main effect of this was to reduce, still further, concern for the role of socio-environmental factors, such as housing, pollution, income and employment, in determining a person's health status and to pay more attention to individual factors, such as health behaviour, thereby increasing the likelihood of 'victim blaming'. In other words, 'the locus for change which might improve the public health had clearly shifted to the person and away from society.' Consequently, 'the very hallmark of the public health tradition from the nineteenth century' had been lost.[26]

The 'New' Public Health

Given the malaise which afflicted public health in this country in the 1970s and early 1980s it is not really surprising that the impetus for the 'new' public health initially came from overseas. Two developments, in particular, are usually seen as the catalysts for change. The first of these was the release of a working document, entitled *A New Perspective on the Health of Canadians*, by the Canadian Ministry of National Health and Welfare in 1974. This document spelt out the essentials of a health care policy for Canada based on the principles of prevention. Some would argue that, in so doing, it marked 'a turning point in efforts to rediscover public health in developed countries'.[27] The second development was the acceptance by the World Health Assembly in 1981 of the WHO's *Global Strategy of Health for All by the Year 2000*. Underlying this strategy is a commitment to ensure that by the year 2000: 'all people in all countries should have at least such a level of health that they are capable of working productively and of participating actively in the social life of the community in which they live.' In order to achieve this goal the WHO has emphasised the importance of ensuring the provision of basic social resources for health and of reorienting health services towards community based provision.

Underlying these developments is the fact that the 'new' public health movement is one of the most visible responses to the 'crisis in health', which is affecting all developed countries. Of particular importance in this respect is the contribution which public health initiatives can make towards raising the profile of the social approach, tackling inequalities and addressing environmental issues.

The 'new' public health movement has provided a home for many academics and practitioners who are disillusioned with the overreliance on the biomedical approach to health and who are actively seeking to put the principles of the **social approach** into practice. For example, in writing about the Healthy Sheffield 2000 initiative the first co-ordinator commented that it was 'based on a social model of health', with one of its underlying objectives being the identification of 'the diverse and interacting social, economic, environmental and personal factors which influence health'.[28]

This does not, however, imply a complete rejection of the biomedical approach, with its emphasis on cure and symptom relief. Many associated with the 'new' public health movement hope that by acknowledging 'the multiplicity of influences which affect the health of the public', they will be able to overcome the traditional 'rivalry between preventive and curative medicine'.[29] For example, hip replacements and the use of drugs in terminal care illustrate the way in which the biomedical and social approaches can be integrated in the 'best interest' of the patient. This was the position adopted by Acheson and his colleagues. In their view, public health as an activity included 'not only efforts to preserve health by minimising and where possible removing injurious environmental, social and behavioural influences, but also the provision of effective and efficient services to restore the sick to health, and where this is practicable, to reduce to a minimum suffering, disability and dependence.'[30]

The desire to tackle the problem of **inequality** in health status, lies at the heart of many 'new' public health initiatives. For example, a review of the annual reports of directors of public health (DsPH) shows that a number of health authorities (e.g. Northampton, Milton Keynes, Salford and Bristol and Weston), in collaboration with other agencies, are now explicitly addressing inequalities within their districts and seeking ways of promoting equal opportunities in health.[31] As commendable as this is, such initiatives will be effective only if they are buttressed by policies to equalise income. These may begin to gather momentum, because the well off have a stake in social equality and therefore have good reason to support the public health movement. As Quick and Wilkinson have indicated 'the health benefits of (income) redistribution are too large to be accounted for in terms of health gains among the poor alone'.[32]

With respect to **environmental issues**, Moore makes the point that just as 'slum housing, contaminated water and polluted air were some of the factors that prompted the first public health movement ... sadly, more than a century later, those same issues are among the problems fuelling the second movement.'[33] It is also becoming increasingly clear that: 'New threats to the public health emerge with technological change and the changing pattern of industrial production and consumption'.[34] For example, lead in petrol, asbestos and nuclear waste have all emerged as environmental issues since 1945. Even those educated within the biomedical tradition are coming to recognise the importance of environmental factors in health. The BMA's report, *Hazardous Waste and Human Health*, is a good illustration in this respect.[35] In drawing attention to socio-environmental concerns of this kind and in campaigning for an appropriate response from the government, the 'new' public health movement is following in the footsteps of the 'old'.

Most of the points made above are reflected in the following quotation from Ashton and Seymour, which summarises the essential features of the 'new' public health:

> *...(It) is an approach which brings together environmental change and personal preventive measures with appropriate therapeutic interventions, especially for the elderly and disabled. However, the New Public Health goes beyond an understanding of human biology and recognizes the importance of those social aspects of health problems which are caused by life-styles. In this way it seeks to avoid the trap of blaming the victim. Many contemporary health problems are therefore seen as being social rather than solely individual problems; underlying them are concrete issues of local and national public policy, and what are needed to address these problems are 'Healthy Public Policies' - policies in many fields which support the promotion of health. In the New Public Health the environment is social and psychological as well as physical.*[36]

In their view the concept which encapsulates the 'new' public health is health promotion, which has been defined by the WHO as 'the process of enabling people to increase control over and improve their health'. At the heart of this concept are a number of key principles, all of which have a particular relevance for those engaged in community health care.

The first principle is that policy makers at all levels and in every type of organisation should give full consideration to the implications for health of their actions. In the words of the *Ottawa Charter for Health Promotion*: 'health promotion goes beyond health care and makes health an agenda item for policy makers in all areas of governmental and organisational life.'[37] Activities such as the collection of taxes, the distribution of benefits, the purchase of goods and services, the employment of staff and the regulation of business and industry are not health neutral. Policy is always more or less healthy and needs to be made more visibly so, through the application of measures such as health impact analysis and performance review which incorporates public health targets.

In the pursuit of 'healthy policies', CHSs staff have an important part to play. They often see at first hand the adverse consequences of 'unhealthy policies'. As a result they can be said to have a duty to ensure that policy makers at national level and elsewhere are made aware of these and ways in which damage to health can be avoided (e.g. health care problems arising from homelessness and the consequent need to invest in low cost housing) and in this way contribute to the calculation of the 'greatest good of the greatest number'. Moreover, through local initiatives they are in a position to demonstrate how policies can be used to secure positive health outcomes (e.g. award schemes to encourage restaurants to produce healthy menus; healthy shopping programmes).[38]

Second, inherent in the concept of health promotion is the principle of community participation. This means that the members of communities, either in a geographical sense or in terms of shared interests or needs, should participate in the planning, management and monitoring of health care. In order to put this principle into practice health care professionals have to find ways of working with communities rather than for them. It is also necessary for the participants to be equipped with an appropriate range of organisational and clinical skills. Thus, CHSs staff may be called upon to act as facilitators in respect of the establishment and maintenance of self-help groups and community health projects, where people identify their priorities for health using their implicit knowledge so that their capacity to act effectively is enhanced.

With respect to participation at the level of the individual, the principle of self-determination should be applied. Individuals should have as much freedom as possible, with the aim of policy being 'to make the healthier choices the easier choices'. In this way the pursuit of 'best interest' can be reconciled with respect for 'personhood'. Again many CHSs staff are strategically placed to facilitate self-determination and to work with local people in identifying and overcoming barriers to healthy living.

A third principle is that of collaboration at every level (i.e. intersectoral, organisational, service delivery). This is essential because of the multifaceted nature of health and the wide variety of agencies, groups and health care workers involved. In view of the experience they have gained from previous cooperative enterprises, CHSs staff are well placed to articulate the prerequisites for effective collaboration namely: common interests and goals, mutual respect, sharing of information, informal networks, and formal mechanisms.

Whereas many would accept the value of these principles, there are those who exhibit a degree of scepticism as to their likely implementation. For example, in *Changing the Public Health* the view is expressed that as a general 'vision' of a desirable future, health promotion 'may be both seductive in the promise it appears to hold and frustrating in the evasiveness of the answers and practical recommendations which it provides.'[39] Nevertheless, attempts are being made to operationalise the concept of health promotion and it is to these that attention is now turned.

Tangible Expressions of the 'New' Public Health

Clearly any attempt to apply the precepts of the 'new' public health will have significant implications for the CHSs. At the very least it will mean a reassessment of priorities, objectives, working practices and relationships. It is therefore essential for those concerned about the future of the CHSs to give serious consideration to: the manner in which the government has responded to the recommendations of the Committee of Inquiry into the Future Development of the Public Health Function chaired by Dr (now Sir) Donald Acheson, who was at the time the Chief Medical Officer; the proposals contained in *The Nation's Health*; the impact of the WHO's European Strategy; and the contents of *The Health of the Nation*.

The Acheson Recommendations

The government's acceptance, in 1988, of the major recommendations of the Acheson Report was an important step towards the operationalisation of some of the key principles of the 'new' public health. Health authorities were required to appoint a DPH and to adopt a clear and explicit public health strategy, 'in which investment in health promotion and disease prevention is perceived as being as fundamental to running a cost effective and rational health service as investment in a new hospital.'[40] For some CHSs staff this development opened up new opportunities by focussing on areas of health care with which they were typically associated. Thus, as Chambers pointed out, those health authorities which had 'a lively community medicine department, led by someone who (was) able to work closely with the district's health promotion and community unit; whose staff (had) good links with the FPC, the local GPs and a variety of officers in the local authority; and who are accustomed to turning their analyses of hard data into realistic recommendations for action'[41] would experience little difficulty in responding to the Acheson recommendations.

The role of DsPH was further clarified in a professional letter issued by the Chief Medical Officer in 1990. They were to be advocates for the community and facilitators of multisectoral collaboration, which is so central to the 'new' public health. Their annual reports were to be an integral part of the planning and commissioning cycle but at the same time retain a degree of independence. They were to include information for local authorities, other bodies and the resident population on local health issues and 'to inform each district, ... FHSA and regional health authority about the health of the population for which they are responsible, to report progress and to identify areas for further improvement, making practical recommendations as far as possible'.[42]

On the face of it the Acheson Report lost some of its initial force with the implementation of the proposals contained in *Working for Patients*. However, the notion of needs assessment, which underpins the commissioning function has important implications for the roles of DsPH (see Chapter 5). Ham and Mitchell have argued that *Working for Patients* offers DHAs the opportunity to 'think radically and imaginatively about the community's needs' and thereby promote the cause of public health. Moreover, health authorities 'may be able to avoid provider capture and take on the role of community advocates in establishing expenditure priorities.'[43] Similarly, some planners have seen the requirement to prepare service specifications as a real opportunity for developing a public health approach and shifting the balance of resources and service provision away from the acute services and towards services for the priority groups and the CHSs.[44]

Although this is a narrower conception of health care planning than many proponents of the 'new' public health might like, it does take an essential step towards making public health considerations prominent in the letting of contracts. It brings DsPH in from the periphery of the health care system and underlines the importance of central government backing for public health initiatives at district level. The CHSs have everything to gain from a development of this kind which is likely to expose more of the 'iceberg' of sickness and disability and to bring into the open the underresourcing of the community sector.

However, it will take a number of years to develop the needs based information systems implied by the Acheson recommendations and until these are in place commissioning authorities will have to rely on information supplied by the provider agencies, based on the previous year's activity levels, as a surrogate for need. It also remains to be seen how far government intervention to protect funding for teaching hospitals and the acute specialties will limit the ability of commissioning authorities to build up community based services.

Nevertheless, if improving and safeguarding public health does eventually become 'the cornerstone of policy determination',[45] the long-term prospects for community health care will be relatively good. Moreover, the omens are promising since a considerable amount of groundwork has been undertaken by those associated with *The Nation's Health* initiative and the WHO's European Strategy.

The Nation's Health

The authors of *The Nation's Health: A Strategy For The 1990s* provided a thorough and wide ranging account of the patterns of health, illness and disability. They called for a national approach to health promotion and the prevention of illness and disability and identified realistic targets based on the known effectiveness, efficiency and political feasibility of interventions in relation to the determinants of health and disease. They also indicated which agencies should be involved and whether initiatives should be centrally or locally instigated.

Although they did not refer specifically to the CHSs, their strategy contains a large number of targets (to be achieved by the year 2000 or earlier) and recommendations of particular significance for those health authority employees who work in community settings. Some examples of these recommendations are set out below.

In relation to **'lifestyles for health'**:

- 'There should be a named community physician or health education officer with responsibility for overseeing the implementation and monitoring of (a) smoking and health policy.'
- 'The promotion of healthy nutrition and the reduction of diet-related disease should be a clearly stated part of regional and district health promotion plans, (which) should include provision of healthy food alternatives for patients and staff in health authority premises ...(and) provision of dietary advice in suitable health authority settings, including antenatal and child health clinics.'
- 'More support should be given to community agencies concerned with those who wish to reduce their drinking.'
- 'The promotion of physical activity should be part of health authorities' strategic and district plans.'
- 'The prevention of sexually transmitted disease and unwanted pregnancy should form part of an integrated approach to the promotion of healthy sexual relationships.'
- 'Every DHA should have a scheme for linking the loan of secure low priced, baby seats in cars to either antenatal or postnatal clinics.'

In relation to **'preventive services for health'**:

- Maternity services should be based on the recommendations of the Maternity Services Advisory Committee and be subject to monitoring and ... 'adequate arrangements should be made to ensure that women in low risk categories are able to have a home delivery.'[46]
- Immunisation programmes should incorporate specific targets, with 'a nominated member of the health authority staff being given overall responsibility for overseeing and implementing (it) and ... an immunisation advisory service for parents who wish to discuss their concerns with a trained nurse or community physician.'
- 'A person of sufficient expertise (usually the community dental officer) should be designated as responsible for overseeing local

policy to promote dental health, in particular the fluoridation programmes.'

- 'Information and counselling should be seen as an integral part of every district ... (early cancer detection) screening service ...'
- Every health authority, in collaboration with other agencies, 'should set clearly defined targets for both the reduction in the population with high blood pressure and screening rates to be achieved in this population over a five year period.'[47]

Despite their worthiness, these recommendations and the strategy, of which they form a part, are less robust than might have been expected, given the concern expressed by the authors of *The Nation's Health* about inequalities in health and the links between poverty and ill health. For example, attention is drawn to the fact that: 'Almost all health indicators confirm the association between the prevalence of ill health and poor social and economic circumstances' and that 'past improvements in health have appeared more as a by-product of a rising standard of living than as a result of conscious policies to improve health'.[48] Nevertheless, in producing their strategy the authors felt unable to include measures designed to improve the living standards of those at greatest risk, such as income maintenance.[49] By contrast the WHO's initiatives are not constrained in this way and are based on the assumption that in order to promote health it is necessary to meet basic human needs by whatever means are at the disposal of governments.

The WHO's European Strategy

Although the WHO's European Strategy shares with *The Nation's Health* the commitment to timed targets, it is based on a much broader vision. This involves not only a more extensive role for national governments but also a European and global dimension.

The European Strategy has been developed within the framework of the WHO's HFA initiative. Underlying this is the premise that groups of countries, individual countries, regions within countries and cities should develop their own stategies for achieving the ultimate goal of HFA by the year 2000. For Europe, the 38 HFA targets (see Figure 6.2), prepared by the WHO's Regional Office, were endorsed by all 33 member states in 1984.

The 38 Targets for the WHO European Region

1. By the year 2000, actual differences in health status between countries and between groups within countries should be reduced by at least 25 per cent, by improving the levels of health of disadvantaged nations and groups.
2. By the year 2000, people should have the basic opportunity to develop and use their health potential to live socially and economically fulfilling lives.
3. By the year 2000, disabled persons should have the physical, social and economic opportunities that allow at least for a socially and economically fulfilling and mentally creative life.
4. By the year 2000, the average number of years that people live free from major disease and disability should be increased by at least 10 per cent.
5. By the year 2000, there should be no indigenous measles, poliomyelitis, neonatal tetanus, congenital rubella, diphtheria, congenital syphilis or indigenous malaria in the Region.
6. By the year 2000, life expectancy at birth in the Region should be at least 75 years.
7. By the year 2000, infant mortality in the Region should be less than 20 per 1000 live births.
8. By the year 2000, maternal mortality in the Region should be less than 15 per 100,000 live births.
9. By the year 2000, mortality in the Region from diseases of the circulatory system in people under 65 should be reduced by at least 15 per cent.
10. By the year 2000, mortality in the Region from cancer in peopleunder 65 should be reduced by at least 15 per cent.
11. By the year 2000, deaths from accidents in the Region should be reduced by at least 25 per cent through an intensified effort to reduce traffic, home and occupational accidents.
12. By the year 2000, the current rising trends in suicides and attempted suicides in the Region should be reversed.
13. By 1990, national policies in all member states should ensure that legislative, administrative and economic mechanisms provide broad intersectoral support and resources for the promotion of healthy lifestyles and ensure effective participation of people at all levels of such policy-making.
14. By 1990, all member states should have specific programmes which enhance the major roles of the family and other social groups in developing and supporting healthy lifestyles.
15. By 1990, educational programmes in all member states should enhance the knowledge, motivation and skills of people to acquire and maintain health.

16. By 1995, in all member states, there should be significant increases in positive health behaviour, such as balanced nutrition, non-smoking, appropriate physical activity and good stress management.
17. By 1995, in all member states, there should be significant decreases in health-damaging behaviour, such as overuse of alcohol and pharmaceutical products; use of illicit drugs; dangerous chemical substances; dangerous driving and violent social behaviour.
18. By 1990, member states should have multisectoral policies that effectively protect the human environment from health hazards, ensure community awareness and involvement, and effectively support international efforts to curb such hazards affecting more than one country.
19. By 1990, all member states should have adequate machinery for the monitoring, assessment and control of environmental hazards which pose a threat to human health, including potentially toxic chemicals, radiation, harmful consumer goods and biological agents.
20. By 1990, all people of the Region should have adequate supplies of safe drinking-water, and by the year 1995 pollution of rivers, lakes and seas should no longer pose a threat to human health.
21. By 1995, all people of the Region should be effectively protected against recognised health risks from air pollution.
22. By 1990, all member states should have significantly reduced health risks from food contamination and implemented measures to protect consumers from harmful additives.
23. By 1995, all member states should have eliminated major known health risks associated with the disposal of hazardous wastes.
24. By the year 2000, all people of the Region should have a better opportunity of living in housing and settlements which provide a healthy and safe environment.
25. By 1995, people of the Region should be effectively protected against work-related health risks.
26. By 1990, all member states, through effective community representation, should have developed health-care systems that are based on primary health-care and supported by secondary and tertiary as outlined at the Alma-Ata conference.
27. By 1990, in all member states, the infrastructures of the delivery systems should be organised so that resources are distributed according to need, and that services ensure physical and economic accessibility and cultural acceptability to the population.

28. By 1990, the primary health-care system of all member states should provide a range of health promotive, curative, rehabilitative and supportive services to meet the basic health needs of the population and give special attention to high risk, vulnerable and under-served individuals and groups.
29. By 1990, in all member states, primary health-care systems should be based on co-operation and teamwork between health-care personnel, individuals, families and community groups.
30. By 1990, all member states should have mechanisms by which services provided by all sectors relating to health are co-ordinated at the community level in the primary health-care system.
31. By 1990, all member states should have built effective mechanisms for ensuring quality of patient care within their health care systems.
32. Before 1990, all member states should have formulated a research strategy to stimulate investigations which improve the application and expansion of knowledge needed to support their national 'Health for All' developments.
33. Before 1990, all member states should ensure that their health policies and strategies are in line with 'Health for All' principles and that national legislation and regulations make their implementation effective in all sectors of society.
34. Before 1990, member states should have a managerial process for health development geared to the attainment of 'Health for All' actively involving communities and all sectors relevant to health and accordingly, ensuring preferential allocation of resources to health development priorities.
35. Before 1990, member states should have health information systems capable of supporting their national strategies for 'Health for All'.
36. Before 1990, in all member states, the planning, training and use of health personnel should be in accordance with 'Health for All' policies, with emphasis on the primary health-care approach.
37. Before 1990, in all member states, education should provide personnel in sectors related to health with adequate information on national 'Health for All' policies and programmes and their practical application to their own sectors.
38. Before 1990, all member states should have established a formal mechanism for the systematic assessment of the appropriate use of health technologies and of their effectiveness, efficiency, safety and acceptability, as well as reflecting national health policy and economic restraints.

Figure 6.2

The 38 targets are now being revised in the light of experience and of insights gained from the ongoing process of analysing health problems. They continue to locate health in an ecological context and to be based on a commitment to 'equitable access to healthy environments'. Proposed revisions of particular significance for this book relate to ethics (discussed in Chapter 2) and women (see Chapter 3). For example, with respect to the latter, it is proposed that target 8 become: 'By the year 2000, there should be sustained and continuing improvement in the health of all women'.[50]

In this country, the pursuit of many of the targets requires the willing and enthusiastic participation of CHSs staff. This must be based on an understanding of the principles underlying the HFA targets and the way in which they are likely to impact upon services. A first and fundamental principle is the high priority given to the reduction of inequalities in health status generally (see target 1) and in relation to particular groups. These include the elderly (target 6), children and young people (target 7) and women (target 8). In the case of each of these targets, the proposed revision would broaden the original objective to encompass all aspects of the health of these groups. For example, the revised target 7 would read: 'By the year 2000 the health of all children and young people should be improved giving them the opportunity to grow and develop to their full physical, mental and social potential.'[51] A concern with equity in health is consistent with the findings of the Black Committee and of Whitehead and others (see Chapter 1) that, even though the health of the population as a whole has improved, the gap between the most healthy members and the least healthy has been widening. Moreover, the targets are based on the assumption that this gap can be narrowed only by means of public policy initiatives and resource allocation measures designed to improve the health of the most disadvantaged groups (see, for example, target 28). Significantly, many members of these groups, such as elderly people on low incomes, are already clients of the CHSs. Thus, those working in community settings have an important part to play in documenting the links between health need and material deprivation. They should also be at the forefront of efforts to secure the adoption, at both national and local level, of the robust research and information strategies that are needed to underpin any moves towards greater equality in health status.[52] Unfortunately, in the proposed revision of target 28, the reference to 'high risk, vulnerable and under-served individuals and groups' is dropped.

A second principle is that health status should be judged by the individual's ability to participate in the activities of daily living as well as medically defined clinical status (targets 2 and 3). This principle has long been applied within the CHSs. For example, the school health service was established, in part, to ensure that the education of children was not hindered by poor health.

Third, the approach to health promotion should be broadly based. It should be directed not only at conditions caused by biological pathogens (targets 5, 9 and 10), but also to the reduction of accidents[53] and health damaging behaviour (targets 11, 12, 15, 16 and 17). The importance of such an approach for CHSs staff is self-evident, since traditionally health promotion has been a major aspect of their work and more recently many of them have been at the forefront of the drive to secure a higher profile for health promotion.

Fourth, there is a need for government commitment and action in respect of the prerequisites of health, such as suitable housing, employment, clean water, adequate sanitation and the absence of environmental hazards (targets 19 to 25). For public policy in these areas to be successful, there has to be a 'bottom up' rather than a 'top down' process of policy making, within the framework set by the targets. Members of the lay constituency must have every opportunity to participate (target 13) and thereby influence the disposition of social resources for health. In so doing they may well need support from community based health care professionals.

Fifth, services should be planned and delivered systematically and in ways which ensure that the needs of all groups are met (targets 27, 28, 31, 32, 34, 35 and 37). In certain respects, CHSs staff are strategically placed to contribute to the application of this principle. For example, health visitors are in a good position to contribute to the identification of the health care needs of minority groups and to assess the effectiveness of existing services in relation to these groups.

The sixth principle is that of teamwork and intersectoral collaboration (targets 29 and 30). For the CHSs the importance of breaking down organisational and professional boundaries has long been recognised but so also have the problems and dilemmas inherent in moving towards a more integrated approach to service planning and delivery.[54] Sadly, in the proposed revisions of these targets there is no explicit reference to teamwork and intersectoral collaboration in health care.

Finally, 'health care systems should be based on primary health care and supported by secondary and tertiary care' (target 26). Whereas in the UK primary health services and CHSs are not synonymous, CHSs staff currently represent the largest single contingent of health professionals working in community settings and are therefore in a pivotal position with regard to the delivery of primary health services.

The successful application of all these principles implies a reversal of the existing relationship between community and hospital based services by making the non-hospital services the cornerstone of the formal health care system. It also requires the construction of health enhancing public policy to strengthen the capacity for self-determination on the part of individuals and communities. At the collective level this involves cooperation between public agencies for particular geographical areas and groups with specific interests. The whole Strategy is shot through with the spirit of egalitarianism. There is a clear commitment to ensuring that everyone has access to health.

Notwithstanding the idealism inherent in the WHO's European Strategy, efforts are being made to convert it into reality, not least through management action. It is significant, for example, that the Institute of Health Services Management and Faculty of Community Medicine have jointly produced a HFA management action pack, in which general managers are given guidance on the steps they need to take to give practical expression to the targets and are encouraged to incorporate HFA principles into 'performance plans and the IPR process.'[55] Moreover, City and Hackney Health Authority has shown that it is possible to combine the breadth of vision of the European Strategy with the realism and practicality of the management action pack by producing a local strategy based on epidemiologically informed priorities drawn from the annual reports of the DPH. Along with a variety of other agencies, it has set imaginative health process targets to be reached within a two year period.[56]

The influence of the WHO's European Strategy can also be seen at national level. Perhaps the best example of this is *The Health of the Nation.*

The Health of the Nation

Two of the key policy objectives and guiding principles underpinning the detailed proposals contained in this document are:

- 'to focus as much on the promotion of good health and the prevention of disease as on the treatment, care and rehabilitation of those who fall ill or need continued support';
- 'to recognise that as health is determined by a wide range of influences - from genetic inheritance, through personal behaviour,

> family and social circumstances to the physical and social environment - so opportunities and responsibilities for action to improve health are widely spread from individuals to Government as a whole'.[57]

Both of these reflect a view of health care which is similar to that of the WHO, but significantly different from that associated with the biomedical and curative approach which has been so influential in the past. So does the suggestion that the central element in the government's strategy should be the identification and agreement of 'specific targets for improvements in health.'[58]

The importance attached to the setting of targets is demonstrated by the fact that much of the green paper is devoted to the selection of key areas for this purpose[59] and a consideration of possible targets. Not surprisingly, the key areas are:

- causes of substantial mortality (e.g. coronary heart disease, accidents);
- causes of substantial ill health (e.g. diabetes, asthma);
- factors which contribute to mortality, ill health and healthy living (e.g. diet, alcohol, physical exercise);
- those where there is room for improvement (e.g. health of pregnant women, infants and children, environmental quality); and
- those where there is a great potential for harm (e.g. HIV/AIDS, food safety).[60]

In most cases there is scope for improved performance and therefore setting targets is both realistic and constructive. Moreover, it is significant that many of the suggested areas for target setting are those in which CHSs staff have a particular interest and expertise.

However, in spite of the positive features of the green paper, it is not without its shortcomings. As many commentators have pointed out, the most serious of these is its failure to acknowledge that one of the major causes of ill health and of inequalities in health status is poverty.[61] Blackburn, for example, argues that any 'strategy that aims to improve family health and the ability of families to meet their own needs should have family poverty as its central concern.'[62] Moreover, although the green paper makes reference to variations in the incidence of illness,[63] it ignores the evidence mentioned earlier which suggests that, in order to improve the health of the nation as a whole, it is necessary to address the unequal distribution of income. As Wilkinson and others have asserted, equalising income would not only reduce inequalities but would improve health overall.[64] Thus, if public health measures are to have an impact they must be buttressed by genuine attempts to secure a more equitable distribution of income.

The green paper has also been criticised by health economists on the grounds that it is misguided and lacks scientific credibility. They claim that many of the targets are based on inadequate evidence and that too little consideration has been given to the mechanisms for achieving them. Likewise, the cost-effectiveness of certain preventive programmes, such as breast cancer screening and anti-smoking campaigns, is challenged. In their view, districts should be able to set their own health promotion targets reflecting local circumstances and priorities.[65] Flexibility in adapting the national framework to local problems and priorities is very much in keeping with the spirit of the 'new' public health movement.

In conclusion, it can be argued that all the developments considered in this section provide those seeking to redefine community health care and to find new ways of planning and delivering services with a 'window of opportunity'. How this might be used is explored in the next section.

The Principles of the 'New' Public Health and the Community Health Services

By now it should be clear that public health involves taking action in the wider political and socio-economic systems to secure the basic resources for health, such as appropriate and safe housing, adequate income and supportive social networks. This would clearly have implications for the CHSs. It would involve the adoption of a broader perspective in planning and service delivery. Moreover, if the strategy is to be effective, policies should be developed through extensive participation by the local population,[66] with statutory and voluntary agencies working on a patch basis. Local priorities and targets should be compatible with those determined nationally and should take account both of the resources available and of research findings on the effectiveness of provision with respect to activities of daily living and clinical status.

The CHSs are, in many respects, well primed for the application of the principles of the 'new' public health. Nevertheless, the staff involved would need to make some adjustments to their working practices and to their priorities. These can be illustrated by reference to: the nature of health encounters;[67] the status of service users; the education and training process; and management and resource allocation.

The Nature of Health Encounters

Health encounters would have to be viewed and planned as a developmental series, with particular attention being given to the maintenance or enhancement of health potential. This contrasts with the traditional biomedical approach which sees clinical encounters as visits to practitioners initiated by individual patients responding to discrete episodes of ill health. The encounters would also be 'holistic' rather than reductionist in their orientation, with due respect being given to the 'personhood' of service users and informal carers. In other words, they would tap the implicit knowledge of clients with a view to identifying a range of factors adversely affecting their health (e.g. low income, poor housing). Moreover, wherever possible, action would be taken to deal with factors of this kind by securing support from appropriate quarters (e.g. welfare rights organisations, housing associations). The philosopy underlying the Peckham Health Centre, discussed by Scott-Samuel, is illustrative of what might be achieved in this respect.[68]

Clearly, such health encounters, imply a continuous relationship between service provider and user and one which is much closer than that usually contemplated. To be practicable, more staff time and energy than at present would have to be devoted to working with groups rather than solely individuals. This might involve work with those who share a clinical condition (e.g. multiple scelerosis, diabetes, depression); those in a particular gender/age category (e.g. middle aged women, young mothers, unemployed men); or those whose access to current services is restricted by cultural differences and institutionalised racism (e.g. members of the black and Irish communities who find it difficult to obtain the mental health services they need). As Downie and colleagues point out, it is vital to work with '**people** and **places** rather than **problems**' (their emphasis).[69]

In view of their traditions and role, it is not really surprising that health visitors have been at the forefront of attempts to move towards more group based ways of working, which draw upon and legitimise the lived experience of individuals and communities. Drennan, in a series of case studies published in 1988, demonstrated how health visitors have sought to exploit the potential of group work of this kind.[70] For example, they have used it as a means of:

- securing improved access to the prerequisites for health in respect of disadvantaged sections of society;
- instigating a community campaign for a family centre and the involvement of members of the community in its planning; and
- enabling homeless families to identify unmet needs, to establish a 'safe and stimulating environment for the children and their parents' and to play a part in developing support networks.

Similarly, initiatives have been taken by members of the Radical Health Visitors' Group (e.g. organising workshops on contemporary issues of relevance to health visiting practice, such as race and racism, nuclear power and community development; producing leaflets to discourage 'health visitors from allowing themselves to be used as agents for baby milk and baby food manufacturers by promoting free samples').[71] These aim to identify the adverse consequences of the policies of government, business and industry and to push for healthy public policies.

Both the case studies and the initiatives are of particular importance since they illustrate developments within health visiting which could be applied to other groups of community based staff (e.g. school nurses, community dentists, dietitians) and to services generally.[72] In this way service providers would begin to make connections between physical and mental distress and the living and working conditions which people experience and to derive the satisfaction which many of the contributors to the Drennan case studies felt when they, together with their clients, sought to address the underlying social causes of poor health.

From a public health perspective, the effective management of health encounters requires the erosion of traditional professional boundaries and a greater emphasis on multidisciplinary working. In other words, there has to be a far greater acceptance on the part of professionals that they have more to offer by cooperating with members of other professions. They should also resist the temptation to challenge the legitimacy of the contribution of those who do not belong to their profession. Moreover, professionals need to reassess their relations with service users since proponents of the 'new' public health envisage a more active role for the public at large; greater scope for clients to participate in clinical encounters, as equal partners; and a general enhancement of the status and power of users vis-a-vis service providers.

The Status and Power of Service Users

To some extent the enhancement of user status and power will come about through greater contact between service providers and those who are well, and therefore less physically and psychologically vulnerable than they would be in a traditional biomedical encounter. In situations of this kind, the assumptions of service providers regarding 'patient compliance', based on obedience to a regime set by health professionals, will no longer be seen as appropriate. Instead, a more democratic relationship is needed, in which service users actively participate in making decisions affecting their health. Moreover, in this context, there will be a greater obligation on the part of service providers to inform, and a greater desire on the part of users to gain access to reliable information, both formal and informal, about those factors which affect health.

Thus, it would be possible to make decisions about health, whether individual or collective, in the light of: a shared understanding of the influence of social and economic circumstances on lifestyle; the significance of lifestyle for health status; the basic principles of physiology and psychology; the nature of specific health problems; and the options for the management of different syndromes. This implies treating service users as a resource for addressing both their own health needs and those of others in similar circumstances. From a practical point of view, it would also mean making greater use of drop-in centres; increasing self referral to specialist services; and creating more opportunities for former patients to run support groups. Recognition of the positive contribution which users can make to health encounters in this way will clearly enhance their status, reduce their isolation, build their confidence and develop their competence.

Respect for the 'personhood' of users can be taken further by involving them formally in the planning and delivery of services. For example, user representatives could participate in: decisions concerning the allocation of resources; staff selection; setting agendas for health promotion campaigns; and identifying gaps in, and monitoring, services. Moreover, through local health audits residents can determine their priorities with regard to health needs.[73]

Empowering users will intensify the pressures for a more collectivist stance vis-a-vis the needs and problems of those living and working in conditions which are detrimental to their health. In this context, collectivism implies a commitment not only to political action on the part of service providers but also to the mobilisation and resourcing of service users through outreach and advocacy schemes modelled on those developed by community workers in the late 1960s and early 1970s.[74] These schemes can be used to establish links between the formal service providers and those who find the present pattern of services so unacceptable that they do not use them. In this way they may serve to empower those who are alienated from the formal health care system and thereby enlist their support in campaigns to secure a more equitable distribution of health care. Underlying schemes of this kind is 'the belief that the ultimate justification for intervention lies not only in the possibility of tangible outcomes, but also in the learning opportunities (they provide) for the participants, including personal development and the raising of political consciousness.'[75] There is now a wealth of information available on the operation and evaluation of community development processes and projects, which indicates that empowerment of users can be justified on grounds of effectiveness.[76]

Clearly any changes designed to increase the power of the lay constituency will have far-reaching implications for the skills and attributes which service providers will require. In order to cope effectively with the new demands, which a more participative approach to delivering services will place upon them, particular attention will need to be given to their education and training.

Education and Training

It can be argued that the successful application of the principles of the 'new' public health within community health care depends, in part, on the ability of those responsible for the education and training of service providers to develop appropriate courses and programmes. This implies a broader strategy to syllabus design in which as much emphasis is placed on non-clinical, as clinical, knowledge and skills. Service providers require a solid grounding in the social sciences so that they are better able to play a constructive part in the planning and policy making processes. They also need the competence and confidence to engage in a wider variety of interdependent activities than at present. These include:

- collaborating with members of other professions on multidisciplinary enterprises;
- working 'with' service users rather than just 'for' them, tapping their implicit and explicit knowledge and empowering them;
- creating networks of those with common health care interests and concerns;

- producing and disseminating information for use in the planning, monitoring and delivery of services; and
- transfering clinical skills to other professionals and to lay people, which is a repeated theme in the public health literature.

Perhaps the most effective way of helping service providers acquire and develop the skills they need to engage in activities of this kind is through the application of more imaginative and experiential forms of teaching and learning. For example, team work and interpersonal skills are best developed through the setting of group based assignments, involving both peer and group assessment; communication skills through role play exercises; information technology skills through 'hands on' experience; design skills through workshop based activities; and competency in skill transfer by means of simulation.

Inherent in this reassessment of education and training for providers of health care in community settings, is the need to accept that the dependency model of the relationship between client and service provider is no longer valid. Inevitably, this will give rise to feelings of unease, insecurity and vulnerability on the part of professionals. Thus, one of the principal objectives of those involved in education and training must be to help students recognise and understand those hidden aspects of their own motivation which might give them a stake in creating or reproducing dependency.

Education and training alone cannot bring about the organisational and cultural changes needed to underpin moves towards a public health approach to community health care. They require the wholehearted support and encouragement of managers and a willingness on their part to take the lead in pursuing public health goals and to allocate resources in ways which are compatible with the aims and objectives of the 'new' public health movement.

Management Support and Resource Allocation

As has been argued in earlier chapters, the managerial constituency has, in recent years, become more visible and the 'crisis in health' has given rise to greater concern about the allocation of scarce resources.[77] Thus, in order to realise public health goals, management support and action is required in a number of areas, such as structures, values, procedures and politics.

A public health approach requires the creation of **structures** within which a considerable amount of authority and responsibility for budgets can be devolved to the most local level. In this way it should be possible to ensure that those working at the 'sharp end' have the necessary control over resources to respond in the most appropriate manner to health care needs. Inherent in this is a retreat from uniformity and a move towards greater flexibility in service provision. For it to work, senior managers must be able to live with the diversity and uncertainty which is likely to emerge as each community, patch, neighbourhood or group develops its own distinctive programmes.

Although there has been some movement in this direction (with the advocacy of neighbourhood nursing teams by Cumberlege and the introduction of locality management),[78] the districts concerned have been motivated more by the desire to improve the delivery of existing services and to facilitate collaboration with GPs, than to implement the precepts of the 'new' public health movement. In other words, structural change is a necessary but not a sufficient condition for securing a public health orientation in the CHSs. It also requires a culture which is supportive.

Clearly, cultural transformation is a distinct and necessary adjunct to structural change and it will be brought about only if there is a long-term commitment on the part of managers to the promotion of the **values** intrinsic to public health. In practice this means taking steps to ensure that staff appreciate the importance of, and are encouraged to internalise, certain key values such as proaction in service delivery; client access to the prerequisites for health; informality in the provision of services; and cooperation across professional and agency boundaries and with service users. Of particular importance in this respect is the value of equality in health status which runs like a *leit-motif* through the public health literature.

For managers, cultural changes have important implications for the design and operation of administrative systems and **procedures**. Amongst the most relevant, are those for recruiting staff; allocating resources, both financial and human; planning services; collecting, processing and disseminating information; and assessing the performance of staff.

If managers want to break down some of the barriers which currently exist between service providers and users, then they must take seriously the need to recruit those who are culturally acceptable to those sections of society which have been alienated from formal services and who possess the social skills needed to build bridges. In this respect, efforts should be made to build on the experience of advocacy schemes which have sought to realign the balance of power between users and health professionals and to ensure that community voices are heard in policy making arenas. Some districts have already sought to put this into practice by employing health workers recruited from the local community to act as advocates, interpreters and assistants to professional staff. Such workers may be ill equipped to pursue higher paid posts. Therefore attention has to be given to their education, training and career development needs if they are to be able to make their contribution at all levels in the organisation. In short, it is clear that equal employment policies must be pursued vigorously.

Given the emphasis which those committed to the 'new' public health place on working *with* individuals and groups, rather than *for* them, and utilising to the full their explicit and implicit knowledge, lived experiences and insights, managers must take this into account when taking decisions in respect of the allocation of resources. For example, they must provide facilities, such as meeting rooms and reprographic equipment, and timetable staff in such a way that, whenever necessary, they are in a position to engage in outreach activities, such as attending meetings in the evenings and at weekends and building up networks of those with common concerns. In addition, as indicated earlier, those at the sharp end must have maximum flexibility in the spending of their budgetary allocations and therefore procedures should be designed with this in mind

With regard to the planning of services, it is essential for managers to involve not only providers but also users and carers and the community at large and to ensure that service objectives are conceived in terms of wider public health needs and health outcomes. For example, Winn and Quick in *User Friendly Services* refer to the Lambeth local advisory groups and the Pimlico Patch Committee as mechanisms for involving users in the planning and delivery of health care.[79] Responsibility for the design of information systems should also be shared between providers and users (see Chapter 4).

Additionally, action must be taken to ensure that managerial performance is judged according to criteria which incorporate public health goals and not simply those relating to sickness services. As Chambers suggests, if significant steps are to be taken 'towards a truly reoriented NHS' the performance related pay of managers needs to be linked to the achievement of public health objectives such as 'a 50 per cent reduction in hospital admissions for strokes, coronary heart disease, road traffic accidents, and bronchoscopies'.[80]

Finally, managers must not be too fastidious when it comes to **politics**. This means not only tolerating the involvement of staff in 'areas defined by managers as political activity'[81] but also lending their support to campaigns designed to get public health issues onto the political agenda. In the past they have been wary of explicit political involvement. They have been less than encouraging where staff have aligned themselves with organisations, such as the Radical Health Visitors' Group and Radical Midwives' Group, which sought to galvanise their professional associations into political action and to forge links with like-minded bodies (e.g. Child Poverty Action Group, Baby Milk Action Coalition). The Radical Health Visitors' Group, for example, 'saw itself as a ginger group which was prepared to speak out about the profession failing internally to act politically by using its knowledge to pressurise political parties and government for social change and failing externally to speak to the world at large by taking a stand on current issues.'[82]

Clearly, the adaptation of structures, the realignment of values, the modification of procedures and the legitimisation of political action are costly both in financial and human terms. In the words of Chambers: 'Providing support and leadership (for) the development of public health programmes takes time, skill and commitment.'[83]

However, the benefits to be gained from applying the principles of the 'new' public health within the CHSs can no longer be ignored. The likelihood of improvements in the health status of the population and the reduction of inequalities, together with the high financial costs and diminishing marginal returns of personal medical care, make it imperative to give a far higher priority to public health. CHSs staff must play a key role in this respect. They must forge alliances with others who are similarly committed, especially those in the voluntary sector and local government. Both of these have been prominent in the UK HFA Network which has pursued a community development strategy based on 'resourcing grass roots work ... (and) networks and building alliances'.[84] CHSs staff must also become more adept at intervening in policy debates within districts to secure a larger share of resources for community based health care services. Moreover, they must be instrumental in securing the necessary reassessment of traditional modes of service delivery. This means, in effect, making health encounters more collectivist and 'holistic'; enhancing the status and power of service users and respecting their 'personhood'; and ensuring that both education and training programmes and management practices are compatible with, and contribute to, a public health strategy.

A Question of Balance

Clearly, for the CHSs the emergence of the 'new' public health movement presents considerable opportunities. Closer collaboration between CHSs staff and those who are committed to the cause of public health might well result in the wider application of some of their insights and practices within community health care. At the heart of the public health perspective is a widening of the dimensions of health and illness and a broadening of the activities within which health care professionals can legitimately engage. More specifically this would mean:

- increased resourcing for the CHSs to reflect epidemiological trends;
- reorienting clinical encounters away from an overreliance on the curative, biomedical approach and towards a more preventive, socially based approach;
- systematically identifying health and health care targets with a view to addressing seriously the issue of inequalities in health status;
- monitoring progress towards the achievement of these targets;
- greater involvement by individuals, groups and communities in the design and implementation of health and health care strategies, thereby strengthening their contribution to the promotion and maintenance of health;
- renewing the commitment to collaboration and teamwork; and
- legitimising political activity in the pursuit of 'healthy public policies'.

Application of these practices and insights would undoubtedly result in a renewed interest in the CHSs and their revitalisation at the local level and a higher profile nationally for health care in community settings.

However, the success of this depends upon taking on board the legitimate worries of those who do not wish to abandon the long standing and honourable tradition of meeting personal health care needs. There is a danger that if the CHSs adopt a simplistic model of public health this tradition might be undermined. Juxtaposing personal and public health highlights the tension between the strong individual and personal element in many of the CHSs and the collectivist orientation of public health. Some service providers undoubtedly regard a collectivist approach as beyond their remit, while others, who might embrace collective action, could well encounter difficulties in seeking to balance the conflicting demands of personal and public health. Moreover, the situation is exacerbated by concerns over the ability to meet even manifest need with the resources at their disposal.

Although these tensions cannot be ignored, it would be a mistake to see the various positions as mutually exclusive. It might be possible to strike a balance between a wider brief for professionals and managers, incorporating responsibility for the generation of social resources for health, and the roles which CHSs staff have traditionally performed well. This could be achieved through a public health strategy, involving a practical and conceptual realignment within the CHSs. At the practical level, it would mean giving as much attention to activities relating to the prerequisites for health as to those concerned with clinical need. To secure the necessary support and commitment it would be essential to demonstrate that the benefits to be derived from giving a higher profile to public health activities outweigh the costs. At the conceptual level, it would mean according legitimacy to both types of activity.

Nevertheless, the difficulties involved in bringing about such a realignment should not be underestimated. Entrenched values, structures, procedures and professional practices are major obstacles in this respect. However, the CHSs, with their traditions of proaction and health promotion and their central position in the health and social care system (see Figure 1.1), are better placed than the highly individualist FHSs or HSs to contemplate a move towards the ground occupied by the 'new' public health movement.

Notes

1 See, for example:

J. Lewis, *What Price Community Medicine: The Philosophy, Practice and Politics of Public Health since 1919* (Brighton: Wheatsheaf, 1986);
G. Rayner, *Rethinking Public Health : A new agenda for Local Government*, July 1987, conference proceedings;
J. Ashton and H. Seymour, *The New Public Health* (Milton Keynes: Open University Press, 1988);
Public Health in England. The Report of the Committee of Inquiry into the Future Development of the Public Health Function [Chair: Sir D. Acheson], Cm 289 (London: HMSO, 1988);
Public Health Alliance, *Beyond Acheson: an agenda for the new public health* (London: Public Health Alliance, 1988);
A. Smith and B. Jacobson (eds.), *The Nation's Health: A Strategy for the 1990s* (London: Health Education Authority, London School of Hygiene and Tropical Medicine and King Edward's Hospital Fund for London, 1988), a revised and updated version (edited by B. Jacobson, A. Smith and M. Whitehead) was published in 1991;
Research Unit in Health and Behavioural Change, University of Edinburgh, *Changing the Public Health* (Chichester: J. Wiley & Sons, 1989); and
P. Draper, *Reinventing Public Health* (London: Macmillan, 1990).

In addition, there are a number of new journals devoted to public health, such as *Health Matters, Critical Public Health* and *International Journal of Health Promotion.*

2 A key role in the movement is being played by the Public Health Alliance, which was established in 1987. The principal aims of the Alliance are to raise public consciousness about contemporary health problems and their potential solutions and to ensure that public health issues gain entry to, and remain on, the health care and political agendas. For the CHSs it is significant that the first chair of the Alliance was Shirley Goodwin, who was, at the time, General Secretary of the HVA.

3 G. Moran, 'Public Health at Risk', *The Health Service Journal*, 1 June 1989, pp.668-9.

4 In Hackney, for example, there is a Public Health and Primary Care Planning Group which was set up by the health authority, local authorities, FHSA and voluntary agencies in 1988 to facilitate joint activities in public health. For further details, see *The Health Service Journal*, 19 October 1989, pp.1276-7.

Similarly, Healthy Sheffield 2000, which was launched in June 1987 with the aim of encouraging action to improve the health of all those living in the city and to reduce significantly inequality by the year 2000, is a joint initiative between the city council, community health council, council for voluntary service, FHSA and health authority. A formal planning team with representatives from these organisations operates under the auspices of the joint consultative committee. Links with academic organisations, industry and commerce and trade unions have also been established.

5 N. Hall, 'Health: Planning's Forgotten Purpose', *The Planner*, vol.76, no.37, 21 September 1990, pp.13-16.

6 A. Ravetz in one of the nine articles devoted to public health in *Town and Country Planning*, December 1991.

7 For a summary of the main recommendations of the Acheson Committee and the contents of the health circular outlining the government's response, see R. Ottewill and A. Wall, *The Growth and Development of the Community Health Services* (Sunderland: Business Education Publishers Ltd, 1990), pp.373-5.

9 There are 38 targets. See Figure 6.2 for full details.

10 DH, *The Health of the Nation. A Consultative Document for Health in England*, Cmd 1523 (London: HMSO, 1991).

11 P. Stones, *Local Government for Students*, 2nd Edition (London: Macdonald and Evans, 1964), p.144.

12 *Public Health In England*, op.cit., para.1.3.

13 A. Smith and B. Jacobson (eds.), op.cit., p.2.

14 Ibid., p.xv.

15 See, for example, H. Graham, 'Behaving Well: Womens' health behaviour in context' in M. Roberts (ed.), *Women's Health Counts* (London: Routledge, 1990) and P. Townsend, 'Individual or Social Responsibility for Premature Death? Current Controversies in the British Debate about Health', *International Journal of Health Services,* 1990, vol.20, no.3, pp.373-392.

16 T. McKeown, *The Role of Medicine: Dream, Mirage or Nemesis* (Oxford: Basil Blackwell, 1979), p.121.

17 Edwin Chadwick was responsible for preparing the *Report on the Sanitary Condition of the Labouring Population of Great Britain* (1842), which clearly demonstrated that disease and ill health were closely associated with insanitary environmental conditions, and for campaigning for sanitary reforms. Through his campaigns he was instrumental in securing the establishment of a General Board of Health (1848) to supervise the work of local authorities in the field of public health. Chadwick's work and campaigns were taken forward by John Simon, who was initially the MOH for the City of London and subsequently the first Medical Officer to the government.

18 See A. Wohl, *Endangered Lives: Public Health in Victorian England* (London: Methuen, 1983) and S. Finer, *The Life and Times of Sir Edwin Chadwick* (London: Methuen, 1952).

19 J. Ashton and H. Seymour, op.cit., p.17.

20 J. Lewis, op.cit., p.30.

21 M. Morgan, M. Calnan and N. Manning, *Sociological Approaches to Health and Medicine* (London: Croom Helm, 1985), p.173.

22 Research Unit in Health and Behavioural Change, op.cit., pp.3-4.

23 Ibid., p.3.

24 See R. Ottewill and A. Wall, op.cit., esp. pp.216-20.

25 Research Unit in Health and Behavioural Change, op.cit., p.4.

26 Ibid.

27 J. Ashton and H. Seymour, op.cit., p.21.

28 Sheffield Health Authority, *Report of the Director of Public Health 1989*, pp.12-3.

29 *Public Health in England*, op.cit., para.1.3. See also M. Kelly, 'The World Health Organisation's Definition of Health Promotion: Three Problems', *Health Bulletin* 48/4, July 1990, pp.176-80.

30 *Public Health in England*, op.cit, para.1.4.

31 'A Picture of Health (For All)?: the evidence from annual reports on public health', *HFA 2000 News*, Faculty of Community Medicine of the Royal Colleges of Physicians, no.12, May 1990, pp.11-17.

32 A. Quick and R. Wilkinson, *Income and Health* (London: Socialist Health Association/Ruskin College, 1991), p.21.

33 W. Moore, 'Building a Public Health Alliance', *The Health Service Journal*, 23 July 1987, pp.842-3.

34 Public Health Alliance, op.cit., p.6.

35 BMA, *Hazardous Waste and Human Health* (Oxford: Oxford Paperbacks, 1991), pp.191-6.

36 J. Ashton and H. Seymour, op.cit., p.21.

37 WHO, Health and Welfare Canada, Canadian Public Health Association, *Ottawa Charter for Health Promotion* (Copenhagen: WHO, 1986).

38 See B. Jacobson et.al., 'Achieve Your Targets', *The Health Service Journal*, 19 October 1989, pp. 1276-7 and L. Holdridge and J. Lancaster, 'Healthy Eating in Hull', *The Health Service Journal*, 6 December 1990, pp.1820-1.

39 Research Unit in Health and Behavioural Change, op.cit., p.146.

40 J. Chambers, 'Public Health - Whose Job?', *The Health Service Journal*, 2 March 1989, pp.262-3.

41 Ibid.

42 Chief Medical Officer, Professional Letter PL/CMO(90)12, *Annual Health Reports of Directors of Public Health*, 7 December 1990.

43 C. Ham and J. Mitchell, 'A force to reckon with', *The Health Service Journal*, 1 February 1990, pp.164-5.

44 One Professor of Psychogeriatric Medicine, Eileen Murphy, who was also vice-chair of the Mental Health Act Commission, took the post of General Manager of Lambeth and North Southwark Health Authority for exactly this reason. In explaining her subsequent resignation (1990) she spelled out her earlier hopes:

'There was ... a vitally important notion resurrected in Working for Patients - music to the ears of public health physicians and epidemiologists - that health services should be provided for a discrete, local population on the basis of the need for services and with the overall objective of achieving the population's improved health ... (I) perceived the proposals as building ... on the foundations laid by the Acheson Report.'

See E. Murphy, 'Why I resigned', *THS Health Summary*, May 1990.

45 C. Ham and J. Mitchell, op.cit.

46 For details of the Maternity Services Advisory Committee recommendations see *Maternity Care in Action. Part 1 : Antenatal Care : A Guide to Good Practice and a Plan for Action* (London: DHSS, 1982), *Part 2: Care during childbirth (Intrapartum Care) ...* (London: DHSS, 1984) and *Part 3 : Care of the Mother and Baby (Postnatal and Neonatal Care) ...* (London: DHSS, 1985).

47 For full details of the strategy, see *The Nation's Health*, op.cit., pp.229-271.

48 Ibid., pp.105-6 and p.119.

49 The members of the committee identified services for the elderly, adequate income and safe housing as 'public health priorities where the case for action is strong, but where detailed recommendations (were) beyond (their) remit or (their) expertise.' Ibid., p.234.

50 *Updating of the European HFA Targets* (Copenhagen: WHO Regional Office for Europe, 1991). See also, *HFA 2000 News*, Faculty of Community Medicine of the Royal College of Physicians, no.18, Spring 1992, special issue, edited by C. Kelleher, devoted to the revised targets.

51 Ibid.

52 For a pathbreaking study of the health differences in 638 electoral wards and their relationship with material conditions, see P. Townsend, P. Phillimore and A. Beattie, *Health and Deprivation: Inequality and the North* (London: Routledge, 1988).

53 See P. Constantinides, *The Management Response to Childhood Accidents* (London: King's Fund, 1987) and *HFA 2000 News*, Faculty of Community Medicine of the Royal College of Physicians, no.14, Spring 1991, which is devoted to accident prevention.

54 See Ottewill and Wall, op.cit., esp. pp.500-3.

55 *Health for All: A Management Action Pack* (London: The Institute of Health Services Management in conjunction with the Faculty of Community Medicine, undated).

56 For further details, see B. Jacobson, 'Planning an achievable strategy for 'Health For All' in the inner city: the development of local targets', *Health Education Journal*, vol.49, no.4, 1990, pp.171-5.

57 DH, op.cit., p.vii.

58 Ibid., p.viii.

59 Ibid. The stated criteria for selecting key areas are:

'First, the area should be a major cause of premature death or avoidable ill-health (sickness and/or disability) either in the population as a whole or amongst specific groups of people
and
Second, the area should be one where effective interventions are possible, offering significant scope for improvements in health
and
Third, it should be possible to set objectives and targets in the chosen area and monitor progress towards achievement through indicators.' (p.x.)

60 Ibid., p.xi.

61 See, for example, C. Potrykus, 'Government sidesteps poverty issue', *Health Visitor*, vol.64., no.7, July 1991, p.211.

62 C. Blackburn, *Poverty and Health: working with families* (Milton Keynes: Open University Press, 1991), p.164.

63. DH, op.cit., paras.4.14-4.16.

64 See R. Wilkinson, 'Life Expectancy and Income Distribution', *British Medical Journal*, vol.304, 18 January 1991, pp.165-8, and A. Quick and R. Wilkinson, op.cit.

65 See R. Akehurst, C. Godfrey, J. Hutton and E. Robertson, *Health of the Nation: An Economic Perspective on Target Setting* (York: Centre for Health Economics, University of York, 1991).

66 For an example of the way in which lay people can be empowered through involvement in the policy making process, see B. N. Ong, 'Researching Needs in District Nursing', *Journal of Advanced Nursing*, no.16, pp.638-47.

67 See Chapter 2, footnote 2, for an explanation of the meaning of the term health encounter and the reason why it is being used.

68 For further details, see A. Scott-Samuel, *Total Participation, Total Health: reinventing the Peckham Health Centre for the 1990s* (Edinburgh, Scottish Academic Press, 1990).

69 R. Downie, C. Fyfe and A. Tannahill, *Health Promotion: models and values* (Oxford: Oxford Medical Publications, 1990), p.89.

70 According to Drennan 'group work' incorporates a variety of activities. These are:

'1 Teaching health education topics to a group of people in a structured formal manner.
2 Sharing health education in a dialogue with a group that is already formed.
3 Forming and/or supporting groups for the purposes of self-help, mutual support and health information.
4 Becoming part of a group, made up of local people and/or professionals, formed to influence policy and/or services.
5 Coming together as groups of health visitors to enhance their own practice by sharing ideas and/or mutual support.'

V. Drennan (ed.), *Health Visitors and Groups* (Oxford: Heinemann Nursing, 1988), pp.14-15.

71 Ibid., p.110.

72 For another example of how community nurses can work with groups, in this case women whose health has been put at risk by their subordinate position, see J. Orr, 'Community Nursing', in P. Draper (ed.), *Health Through Public Policy* (London: Merlin Press, 1991). For a discussion of issues surrounding community work and public health, see K. Bullingham, 'Public Health and the Community', *Health Visitor*, vol.64, no.2, February 1991, pp.40-3.

73 A good example is the St Pancras ward health and environment audit, which is referred to in D. Pike, E. O'Keefe and S. Pike, 'Camden in the WHO Healthy Cities Project', *The Planner*, vol.76, no.37, pp.17-20. The essential features of the audit are described in the following terms: 'A very large sample of the people in that area have been asked how they perceive the relationship between the environment and their health and well-being. The lead officer in this project is a registrar in community medicine at the Bloomsbury Health Authority but the audit is essentially being run by local people with the statutory authorities providing help and assistance where required. The findings of the audit will be fed into the council's and health authorities' mainstream programmes.' While such initiatives are to be commended, it needs to recognised that there are limits as to what can be achieved by way of public publication. For example, only two people turned up to a public meeting organised by the DPH of City and Hackney Health Authority designed 'to get information from people in Hackney on what they see as priorities for health care'. See *Guardian Society*, 29 April 1992.

74 Schemes of this kind are particularly associated with the 12 Community Development Projects established in areas of urban deprivation by the Home Office in 1969. Community development is, in part, a means of '**helping people** to reexamine critically the society in which they find themselves, to understand ways in which various political and administrative systems work, to acquire skills in self-organisation and more

specific that may be relevant to self chosen projects' (emphasis added), P. Baldock, *Community Work and Social Work* (London: Routledge and Kegan Paul, 1974), p.3. For an example of the application of the principles of community development to health, see L. Adams and J. Smithies, *Community Development in Health Promotion* (London: Health Education Authority, 1990). See also, P. Willmott, *Community Initiatives: Patterns and Prospects* (London: Policy Studies Institute, 1989).

75 Research Unit in Health and Behavioural Change, op.cit., p.121.

76 See, W. Farrant, *Roots and Branches* (Milton Keynes: Open University Press, 1990).

77 For some case studies of the experiences of community managers in mobilising resources, see P. Spurgeon and F. Barwell, *Implementing Change in the NHS* (London: Chapman and Hall, 1991).

78 See Ottewill and Wall, op.cit., esp. pp.361-3 (locality management) and pp.421-34 (Cumberlege Report).

79 L. Winn and A. Quick, *User Friendly Services: Guidelines for Managers of Community Health Services* (London: King's Fund Centre for Health Services Development, 1989).

80 J. Chambers, op.cit.

81 Ibid.

82 J. Spray, 'Case Study 10 : The Radical Health Visitors' Group' in V. Drennan (ed.), op.cit., p.109.

83 J. Chambers, op.cit.

84 For further details, see Community Participation Group of the UK HFA Network, *Newsletter*, March 1991.

CHAPTER 7

Towards a Community Oriented Approach to Health Care

Many of the issues confronting those with responsibility for the management and delivery of community based health care services have acquired a higher profile as a result of the 'crisis in health'. Of particular importance in this respect has been the role of the 'crisis' in opening up for debate certain ethical questions which lie at the heart of contemporary modes of health care. The point was made in Chapter 2 that questions of this type can be expressed in terms of the tension between the concepts of 'personhood' and 'best interest' and the differing standpoints of the major constituencies (i.e. clinical, managerial and lay). Such considerations can help to shed light in a number of areas, such as gender, the acquisition and utilisation of information, planning and the 'new' public health, where ethical factors may not be immediately apparent. Thus, in seeking insights into the nature of issues in community health care, it is important to reflect on the value conflicts inherent within them as well as those aspects of the 'crisis' more obviously associated with them.

In Chapter 1, attention was drawn to the multifaceted nature of the 'crisis' and to the fact that it is causing concern in all industrialised countries, regardless of the manner in which their health care systems are organised and resourced. Britain is therefore not alone in searching for an appropriate response to the challenges thrown up by:

- the increasing awareness of the limitations of the biomedical approach to health and the need to incorporate an understanding of social factors into the development of health policy;
- the changing patterns of morbidity, disability and mortality;

- the lowering of the waterline, with respect to the 'iceberg' of sickness and disability;
- environmental threats to health;
- the 'greying' of the population;
- rising public expectations regarding the quality of health care services;
- inequalities in health status; and
- resource constraints.

Consequently, the influence of various international initiatives, including the WHO's strategy of Health for All by the Year 2000 and the setting of 38 targets by the European Region of the WHO (see Chapter 6), has also been felt in this country. Given the severity of the 'crisis', however, these are no more than a first step. Indeed, all the evidence suggests that far from easing, the pressures arising from certain aspects of the 'crisis' are intensifying. Thus, it is imperative, not only to implement programmes of the kind advocated by the WHO, but also to find ever more imaginative and creative ways of dealing with the 'crisis'. In so doing, it is important to avoid those which smack of pragmatism and those which are likely to exacerbate existing inequalities in health status.

At the heart of this book is the belief that a **community oriented approach** to the provision of health care does offer a way forward. Such an approach draws heavily upon the rich and complex traditions of the CHSs and involves the wider application of values, and the extensive adoption of modes of service delivery, espoused by those who champion them. As one of the more accountable components of the health and social care system, everything possible should be done to broaden their role; to strengthen their position; and to ensure that, whatever the administrative arrangements, the imbalance in health care provision is redressed in favour of a seamless web of community based services. To this end, the status of CHSs staff should be enhanced because they are more likely than other professionals working in community settings, such as GPs and general dental practitioners, to recognise the full potential of an approach of this kind and be willing to do what is necessary to bring it to maturity. Indeed, the commitment and support of those CHSs staff who are steeped in good practice is an important ingredient of a community oriented approach.

In advocating this course of action it is contended that it is the most appropriate response to the 'crisis' and one which offers the best hope for securing equality, economy, effectiveness and efficiency in the management and delivery of health care. It is also sufficiently resilient to withstand the intense pressures that will have to be faced in the years to come.

In order to elaborate on this contention, it is necessary to examine:

- the components of a community oriented approach;
- the prerequisites for this type of approach;
- the factors hindering the adoption of a community oriented approach; and
- those developments which can be seen as expediting such an approach.

In so doing, further reference will be made to many of the key points from earlier chapters.

Components

While a community oriented approach to health care derives its legitimacy and rationale from established practice within the CHSs, it gains much of its strength and vitality from the rethinking which CHSs staff have been prepared to undertake in recent years, partly in response to the prompting of the 'new' public health movement. Thus, the principal components of this approach reflect the contemporary gloss which is now being placed on principles and activities long associated with health care in community settings.

In reviewing these components, an appropriate starting point is the individual health encounter. Inherent in a community oriented approach is the belief that every encounter should encompass two elements. The first is the application of what could be described as a craft skill (an amalgam of clinical expertise and implicit knowledge) by a trained professional. The second, and equally important, element is that of enabling clients to become, as far as possible, responsible for their own health. This view of health encounters requires a shift from a situation where the normal relationship between users and providers is one of dependency to one where it based on partnership between them. Where the principle of partnership prevails, emphasis is placed on the transferability of health care skills as opposed to their exclusivity and making information accessible to users. Such a view is very much in line with the traditions of health visiting and the principles of the 'new' public health. It also reflects the belief that service providers should seek to balance concern for the 'best interest' of their clients with respect for their 'personhood' and should pay more attention to the health maintenance and illness prevention functions. Clearly, this implies a significant departure from some of the cultural norms which underpin the traditional, biomedical approach to health care.

Similar considerations apply where informal carers are involved in the health encounter. Indeed, recognition of the value of informal caring is another hallmark of a community oriented approach. However, as pointed out in Chapter 3, acknowledgment of the contribution made by informal carers is not in itself enough. It must be backed up with practical support if the potential of this form of care is to be realised. Demographic and epidemiological trends mean that more people will require care in the future, with the result that the informal caring role will become more prominent. Moreover, with greater legitimacy being given to the cause of gender equality and the empowerment of the lay constituency, clinicians and managers will be forced to take seriously the needs, demands and implicit knowledge of informal carers.

A community oriented approach to health encounters also means service providers working with groups of clients, as well as individuals, and on a team basis. This would involve the positive application of the collectivist values associated with the concept of 'personhood' (see Chapter 2). Clearly, in such encounters, the values of group empowerment, flexibility, sharing information, openness and equality are of particular importance and the advocacy role, proaction, prevention and community development techniques are likely to acquire greater significance. Likewise, there would be an acceptance, on the part of all involved, of the limits to their competence; the importance of informal information; and the benefits to be derived from working together.

Given the key role which GPs perform in the delivery of community based health care, principles of this kind have significant implications for their working practices and for their relationship with other service providers. They would have to give greater consideration to the 'personhood' of clients, informal carers and fellow professionals and accept a curtailment of their monopoly of the gatekeeping and certification functions. The latter would apply, for example, in cases where patients have a disability or are suffering from chronic illness and the main concern is with activities of daily living (i.e. functional competence) rather than clinical diagnoses. In the main, GPs acquired the roles of gatekeeper and certifier through the exercise of their 'position', rather than their 'expert', power.[1] It can therefore be argued that they are no more qualified and, in certain situations, may be less well qualified than others to determine whether clients should have access to further services. Alternatives, such as the formal involvement of other health care professionals; the use of a 'jury system'; and more opportunity for appropriate self-referral; all offer a way forward in this respect.

Alongside this reassessment of the nature of health encounters, a community oriented approach requires that steps be taken to secure a workforce which is more representative in terms of the socio-demographic composition (i.e. gender, race, disability, class) of the community it serves. A representative workforce would help to secure services which are accessible and acceptable to clients; a significant reduction in sexual, racial and social stereotyping; greater equality in health status; and real improvements in the quality of health care. A move in this direction depends, among other things, on the availability of appropriate information. Additionally, as in other areas of management, it can be facilitated by the setting of timed targets.[2] However, equal opportunities strategies will be unsuccessful if they are pursued in a mechanistic or grudging manner. There needs to be a general acceptance of the view that the removal of those barriers which discriminate against employees and potential employees on grounds of gender, race or disability can improve the overall level of competence and motivation within organisations. Clearly, where the principle of equal opportunities is firmly embedded in the organisational culture, it will be easier to ensure that the values espoused by different constituencies are given due weight in deciding how services are delivered.

Turning from service delivery to policy making and planning and the information systems which underpin them, a community oriented approach would be less hierarchical and would incorporate many more opportunities for lay participation. This would imply giving greater recognition to the implicit knowledge of service providers, informal carers and users. With respect to normative planning, the processes of needs assessment; establishing priorities; target setting; specification preparation; quality assurance; contract letting; and monitoring and evaluation of service effectiveness would be driven from below, rather than above, within a policy framework designed to minimise inequalities in health status. The lay perspective would be recognised as having as much legitimacy as that of other participants. This would help to obviate the danger that commissioning agencies will pursue their own interests rather than those of the population on behalf of whom they are supposed to be commissioning services.

Similarly, business plans would need to reflect the wishes and preferences of the public at large. This could be difficult given that providers of services are primarily concerned with securing contracts from commissioning agencies and in so doing may have little direct contact with the lay constituency. This is clearly undesirable for any form of health care and it is particularly ill suited for community based activities such as health promotion, counselling, long-term care and rehabilitation. Thus, any planning system which does not derive its momentum from below cannot be regarded as appropriate for a community oriented approach.

However, even increased lay involvement in policy making and planning will not overcome the difficulties involved in assessing needs, setting priorities, allocating resources and determining quality standards. Indeed, the inclusion of a wider variety of views is likely to exacerbate them. This is because, as pointed out in Chapter 2, many ostensibly technical questions are in fact ethical issues in disguise and involve making value judgements. Such judgements will reflect not only individual differences of view but also the position of various constituencies with respect to values associated with the concepts of 'personhood' and 'best interest'.

To acknowledge the existence of value conflict and to accommodate the differences between constituencies, a community oriented approach would involve the establishment, at a number of levels, of mechanisms which facilitate the consideration of ethical issues. These would provide forums within which each constituency could be represented; could articulate their position; and could negotiate a course of action in an open and explicit manner. Inevitably, one of the major weaknesses of mechanisms of this kind is the unequal distribution of power between the various interests. While steps can be taken to help the weaker interests play a full part (see Chapter 2), there are limits to what can be achieved in this respect.

Because of the close links between the exercise of power and health, as indicated in earlier chapters a community oriented approach would be characterised by political activity on the part of all the constituencies. This does not mean engaging in party politics. Rather it involves the constant monitoring of the impact of public policy on health status; assessing the effects of company decisions on health; highlighting areas of concern; arguing the case for changes in policy; and putting forward proposals for improving the health status of individuals and communities. Many community based service providers and managers, as well as members of the lay constituency, are uniquely placed to make such a contribution to the political process. They can do so in two main ways. First, they can articulate their views through existing channels of communication, such as professional associations, self-help organisations and other pressure groups. Second, they can exploit opportunities for documenting the implicit knowledge of lay people and front line service providers and thereby increase the likelihood that knowledge of this kind will inform political debate.

Another significant aspect of the political process, which tends to be overlooked, is the allocation of public funds to research. A community oriented approach implies a different set of research priorities from that which has traditionally prevailed. This would mean:

- allocating more funds to the study of epidemiology and social factors in health and health care, thereby reversing the current bias towards research in the biomedical field;[3]
- encouraging the development of systematic qualitative methodologies;[4]
- facilitating long-term studies;
- exploiting the potential of community health staff, especially nurses, in the sphere of research;[5] and
- establishing partnerships between researchers and local communities to enable the latter to set their own research agendas.[6]

Clearly, developments of this kind have a practical as well as a symbolic significance. Research findings are an important source of formal information for the development of a community oriented approach. By shifting priorities, it would be possible to ensure that the benefits of research are more evenly spread amongst the constituencies.

A final component of a community oriented approach would be greater collaboration between the various agencies involved. Whatever the precise administrative arrangements, there is always likely to be a multiplicity of agencies with a legitimate interest in community based health care services. Thus, inter-agency collaboration has to be taken seriously. As Ham points out, one of the ways 'the NHS should deal with the challenges facing it ... (is by) developing healthy alliances with local authorities and other agencies whose actions have a bearing on the health of the population.'[7] In the past, however, the rhetoric has exceeded the reality. Experience demonstrates that, even when there have been incentives, agencies have done little more than pay lip service to the principle of collaboration. Real progress depends upon the use of a variety of devices, alongside cultural changes which can be secured only through the consistent application of an appropriate set of values and a genuine effort to win the hearts and minds of all those involved.[8]

The various components of a community oriented approach, outlined in this section, represent a coherent and realistic strategy for responding to the demographic and epidemiological changes; the public concern over the quality of health care; and the ever widening gap between needs and resources; which lie at the heart of the 'crisis in health'. However, despite the feasibility of a strategy of this kind, it will not be implemented successfully unless certain prerequisites are met.

Prerequisites

Arguably, the first and most important prerequisite is the effective championing of the ideals inherent in the community oriented approach. In the past, CHSs 'were seen as low status and a professional dead-end'[9] and there were relatively few influential figures articulating the principles of partnership, group work, teamwork, collaboration and participation. On the contrary, for most of the twentieth century, the principles of dependency, individualism and authoritarianism have dominated within health care. While this situation has been challenged in recent years, the need for powerful backers strategically located in key political positions within the health and social care system remains essential. For example, the cause would be strengthened if senior figures within the clinical professions (particularly general practice), political parties, educational institutions, the media, health authorities and government departments, fully understood the contribution which a community oriented approach could make in tackling the 'crisis in health'.

With the increasing importance of contractual relationships and the greater commercialisation of health care, progress also depends upon the willingness of commissioners to exercise their power in a manner which is supportive of the principles of community health care. This means, in effect, that when assessing need and preparing their service specifications, commissioners must be willing to collaborate with each other, to incorporate lay perspectives and to classify and define services in such a way that higher priority is given to health maintenance, counselling and caring. They must also take steps to ensure that they perform their role as 'champions of the people' in an imaginative and creative manner and give due attention to the issue of quality; that their information systems are well designed (see Chapter 4); and that providers meet their contractual obligations. Because of the fundamental nature of some of the changes that would be necessary to secure a more community oriented approach, the need for adequate audit/monitoring arrangements, including spot checks and penalties for inadequate performance, is of particular importance.

However, even if there is a high degree of commitment on the part of the commissioners of health care, a great deal still depends upon the ability of providers to deliver. This requires not only appropriate structures and systems but also a sense of ownership and mission with respect to the values inherent in a community oriented approach. While the realisation of such a vision is likely to be facilitated where there are trusts and units with sole responsibility for community based services, the crucial requirements are cultural as much as organisational. Hence the need for attention to be given to the education and training of managers and service providers and to policies governing recruitment, selection and career development. With respect to education and training, future cohorts of clinicians and managers need a thorough grounding in the social sciences and exposure to ethical questions in order to help them avoid the narrowness of view associated with biomedical explanations of ill health and one-to-one health encounters. Additionally, they should learn alongside those preparing for different though related occupations, such as social work, town planning, teaching and housing management. It is also necessary to reinforce educational change by addressing the way in which staff are recruited, selected and developed.

A final prerequisite is a willingness and an ability of members of the lay constituency to become active participants in the health care process. Unless users and informal carers are prepared to work closely with service providers, one of the key objectives of a community oriented approach cannot be met. This may mean taking positive action to overcome the reluctance of many people to see themselves as the partners of health care professionals. In addition, professionals need to learn how to communicate in less patronising ways and thereby become less of a deterrent to full participation by lay people. However, even in situations where all parties are favourably disposed to this approach, clients still need appropriate skills and knowledge before they can participate with any degree of confidence. Moreover, account needs to be taken of the fact that lay participation, by both groups and individuals, incurs costs (e.g. respite or child care, transport), which have to be met if bias, in terms of gender, class, race and disability, is to be avoided.

In outlining these prerequisites, it is recognised that they will not be easy to meet, at least in the short-term. It will be a long haul and there are no short cuts. Ultimate success will depend, in part, on the ability of those concerned to overcome a number of obstacles and to deal with a variety of threats.

Obstacles and Threats

Progress towards a community oriented approach is being, and will continue to be, hindered by obstacles and threats both within and outside the health and social care system. Clearly, these must be acknowledged before they can be effectively tackled.

One of the most potent of the internal threats is the negative and imperialist attitude of many GPs. Traditionally, GPs have shown relatively little interest in encouraging clients to exercise greater control over the determinants of health; in working with groups of clients; in adopting proactive and preventive modes of care; in sharing their expertise; and in appreciating the contribution of other health care professionals. They have also been over-reliant on biomedical explanations of ill health and techniques and slow to explore alternatives. Moreover, because of their unwillingness to forego their independent contractor status, changes in general practice have been secured only by resorting to costly financial incentives. This can be illustrated by reference to their current contract, which incorporates generous allowances to encourage them to become more preventive in their approach[10] and to offer a more comprehensive service by employing a wider range of non-medical professional staff.[11] While any moves towards the development of preventive and comprehensive services are to be welcomed, the evidence suggests that the provisions of the contract are not working in the manner intended. For example, the establishment of health promotion clinics is motivated more by their potential for generating income than for maintaining health.[12] As a result most GPs are taking little, if any, interest in the way in which they are being conducted or in assessing their effectiveness. Similarly, many are using the practice nurses they employ in an inappropriate manner by simply transferring responsibility for narrow, clinically-based tasks to them.

The stance of GPs is particularly important because of their powerful position within the system, both in the direct provision of care and as gatekeepers to other health and social care services. Thus, it is unfortunate that there has been a rapid increase in the number of practice nurses, which many see as a serious threat to the integrity of the traditional community nursing services (e.g. district nursing, health visiting, community midwifery)[13] and that GPs are expanding into fields previously occupied by those who are more sympathetic towards a community oriented approach.

Sadly, those enlightened GPs, such as Tudor Hart, Muir Gray, Jarman, Feder and Dobbing, who have demonstrated, and sometimes documented, ways in which general practice can be improved,[14] have been the exceptions rather than the rule. Despite their idealism and commitment, they have been unable to persuade a majority of their colleagues to follow their lead. This suggests that, for the foreseeable future, any move in the direction of a community oriented approach on the part of GPs will be limited in scope. Consequently, there is a very real danger that biomedicine will continue to intrude inappropriately in both the delivery and content of community based health care services and that GPs will remain elitist in their relationships both with patients and with other professionals.

A similar threat comes from the acute sector. With increasing competition in health care, there is a likelihood that in some parts of the country hospital trusts and units will win contracts for community based services. This is dangerous since many of these trusts/units still lack the necessary commitment to community values and view those working in community settings as their 'hand maidens'. In other words, community services may well be driven from the hospital sector which would not only stifle their growth and creativity but would also damage, perhaps irrevocably, the moves towards a community oriented approach which are already taking place.

Fears of this kind have been forcefully articulated by Hancock. Referring to new models of acute care, which require 'very high levels of domiciliary nursing support', she has expressed concern about the 'one-way vision of acute intervention in hospital followed by recovery and rehabilitation at home'. In her view, the 'future organisation and delivery of primary care and community care services should not be undermined because the acute sector re-oriented community services to care for acutely ill people at home'. The situation will be even worse if trust hospitals employ 'their own community nurses or ... sub-contract to private home nursing services in order to allow safe early discharge and therefore faster hospital throughput'. Moreover, there is a failure to take account of 'the very large number of people with nursing needs who never get as far as an in-patient stay'.[15]

A major internal obstacle is the dearth of political action on the part of those who could be regarded as the natural champions of a community oriented approach. These include the general managers or chief executives of trusts and units responsible for CHSs and senior figures within the community based professions, such as district nursing, speech therapy and chiropody. Part of the explanation for the low level of political activity lies in the scarcity of appropriate skills and a certain amount of naivety regarding the intentions and predilections of GPs and the acute sector. It is also due to a reluctance on the part of prospective champions to participate in the political process, either alone or as members of a coalition, for fear of being identified with a particular faction thereby undermining their perceived neutrality and perhaps, more importantly, their career prospects and job security.

The emergence of managerialism as a potent force within health care has to some extent legitimised the apolitical stance of managers.[16] This has been achieved by presenting issues in technical rather than political terms and by offering a range of techniques for dealing with them. Inevitably, managerialist solutions to health care problems are misguided since they fail to take account of the value conflicts which underlie them and which must be addressed in the political arena. Managerialism has also contributed to the downgrading of clinical skills and expertise. This is particularly serious from the point of view of a community oriented approach with its requirement for a marked shift in the nature of the health encounter and consequently the redefinition rather than the devaluation of professionalism.

Increasing competition between the providers of community based services, which is an inevitable consequence of the moves towards a more commercially based health care system, is another obstacle. In a competitive environment it will be far more difficult for providers (e.g. trusts, DMUs, voluntary organisations) to cooperate in the pursuit of long-term goals relating to changes in the way health care is delivered. For the voluntary sector, it is likely to result in the marginalisation of its traditional campaigning role and of the distinctive contributions of the smaller groups which have developed to fill gaps left by the larger groups and statutory agencies. The pressure will be on providers to offer types of care which can be easily costed and monitored and where apparent 'value for money' can be demonstrated. In other words, short-term, curative, biomedically oriented services, based on the principle of dependency, will predominate and it will become extremely difficult to defend community values.

External threats and obstacles are those rooted in the environment of health care, which encompasses the educational, economic, social and political systems. These play a key role in maintaining the ascendency of biomedicine and, in so doing, perpetuating a culture that is out of tune with the values which underpin a community oriented approach.

Specifically, attempts to support users who seek to play an active role in health encounters and to highlight the ethical and political nature of many aspects of health care, may well be thwarted by changes in the wider world. For example, the introduction of the national curriculum decreases the time available in schools for health education initiatives; the discussion of current affairs; and the examination of value questions. Similarly, the potential reduction in public service broadcasting may mean less coverage of health care and political issues by radio and television in the future.

Social and economic changes affecting patterns of life making social networks more fragile; increasing the stress associated with employment; and contributing to the proliferation of demands on people's time and energy can also be seen as a threat. Under these circumstances, the willingness and ability of members of the lay constituency to acquire and apply appropriate skills and knowledge, in order to become active participants in the health care process, is impaired.

With respect to preventive initiatives, which are so central to a community oriented approach, threats arise from the continuing scarcity of resources, the tenets of the enterprise culture and the power of vested interests. Together, these reduce the ability, and undermine the willingness, of policy makers to invest in health maintenance and promotion programmes where the benefits will not be felt until some time in the future; the outcomes are often intangible; and there are usually heavy political costs. For example, the development of an effective strategy with respect to smoking has proved to be particularly difficult because of the reluctance of governments to go too far in alienating the tobacco lobby; their unwillingness to invest sufficient resources in investigating and dealing with the causes of smoking; and the lack of a clear causal link between the costs and the benefits of anti-smoking programmes and their separation in time and space.

Paradoxically, the community oriented approach might also be under threat from developments within local government. The responsibilities for community care which local authorities have recently acquired (see Chapters 1 and 5), provide them with the means to influence the future direction of health care in community settings. How they choose to exercise this power remains to be seen. The community oriented approach could be well-served if the radical thrust towards user-led services evident in some social services departments were to become typical. However, pressure on resources makes this unlikely. Indeed, when letting contracts for care packages and in case management the need to secure immediate 'value for money' and easily quantifiable outputs might dominate, particularly as there are no incentives to ensure that even basic needs are met. Moreover, in determining priorities, social needs might well take precedence over health needs. Sadly, boundary disputes regarding the distinction between and the responsibility for health and social care needs are already rife.

Last, moves towards a community oriented approach are hindered by the complacency which surrounds public policy on certain aspects of health care. This can be seen in the optimistic claims made by governments with respect to the realisation of various health objectives. One example is the statement made in *The Health of the Nation* that: 'England has in place an established primary health care system based on **teamwork**' (emphasis added).[17] As argued elsewhere, efforts to develop effective primary health teams have been notably unsuccessful.[18] Without a far more realistic assessment of the current position, progress of any kind is likely to be flawed since plans will rest on very shaky foundations.

Nevertheless, while these threats and obstacles are important and should not be underestimated, the situation is not as gloomy as it may appear at first sight. There are some helpful developments which must be set alongside the threats in order to obtain a more balanced view.

Helpful Developments

In some respects the prospects for a significant shift towards a community oriented approach to health care have never been brighter. Various developments can be cited to justify such a view. The increasing awareness and acknowledgement of the 'crisis in health' is, in itself, a positive development. It has contributed to a climate in which there is a greater willingness to consider more radical alternatives to existing patterns of health care. Of particular importance in this respect is the growing unease concerning the costs and limitations of biomedical interventions, which has strengthened the position of those seeking to raise the profile of preventive and social interventions. Moreover, the international dimension of the 'crisis' has exposed domestic policy makers to the initiatives being taken by supra-national organisations and to innovative practices in other countries. Comparative material is not only a source of new ideas, but can also be used to legitimise various aspects of what is described here as a community oriented approach to health care.[19]

Further, as indicated in Chapter 6, during the past few years there have been a number of developments which suggest that the government now recognises the need for a realignment within the health care system, incorporating some of the ideas being promoted by the 'new' public health movement. A major influence on the government's thinking in this respect has undoubtedly been Sir Donald Acheson, the former Chief Medical Officer, who played a key role in pushing for a shift in health policy. Moreover, his successor, Professor Kenneth Calman (appointed in 1991), has publically acknowledged that social and economic initiatives offer greater scope for improving health than those emanating from the NHS. In addition, he has argued that 'expensive or technically difficult procedures should be planned or regulated on a regional or national basis, to avoid their unnecessary proliferation',[20] thereby acknowledging that these are public services, the distribution of which cannot be left to the vagaries of the market.

Arguably, from the point of view of the rediscovery of public health, the most important development in recent years has been the publication of *The Health of the Nation*. Despite the element of complacency referred to earlier and the political nature of a document of this kind, it has the potential to secure major changes in the way that health and health care are perceived and planned. This can be seen in the emphasis placed on: the promotion of good health and the prevention of disease; the recognition that government action is as important as individual responsibility in the pursuit of improvements in health; and the attention given to setting health care objectives and targets. For those committed to a community oriented approach, it is significant that there is a clear acknowledgement of the need to give as much attention to health promotion, disease prevention and after-care as to diagnosis and treatment. It should also be noted that many of the areas of concern, which have been highlighted for target setting,[21] are those where the consideration of social factors and respect for 'personhood' must receive a high priority if progress is to made in dealing with them (see Chapter 6).

Clearly it would be wrong to suggest that *The Health of the Nation* necessarily heralds a new era in health care, since similar documents have proved to be false dawns in this respect. Nevertheless, its publication is a hopeful sign and, because of its timeliness, may yield more tangible results.

Another consideration is that, while moves towards a mixed economy in health can be seen as an obstacle to progress, by raising questions concerning the efficiency of clinical interventions, they may also be regarded as a helpful development. The importance of securing 'value for money' has resulted in a more critical approach to assessing the relative costs and benefits of different kinds of treatment. Both governmental and non-governmental organisations are playing a part in this and are involved in the gathering, collation and transmission of data and information (see Chapter 4) on the basis of which judgements about costs and benefits can be made. For example, the NHS Management Executive is funding initiatives in Leeds and York Universities and the Research Unit of the Royal College of Physicians to produce bulletins on the effectiveness of health service interventions which will provide districts and FHSAs with summaries of the evidence to date on the efficacy and cost-effectiveness of a range of health care interventions and procedures tailored to suit the requirements of commissioners.[22]

Research of this kind is demonstrating that health encounters based on the principles which underlie the community oriented approach are more cost-effective than hospital based encounters. Where clients are enabled to take more responsibility for their own health and where providers work with groups rather than individuals, there is likely to be greater 'value for money'.

In their public pronouncements, a number of RHAs have indicated that they recognise the valuable contribution currently being made by CHSs staff and that they are willing to take on board some of the principles underlying the community oriented approach, as part of a fundamental rethinking of the manner in which services are organised and delivered. For example, in a consensus statement issued in 1991, South East Thames Regional Health Authority drew attention both to the importance of community nurses in the provision of community health care and to various factors which call into question the efficacy of the biomedical and hospital based approach. In so doing, it increased the likelihood of a significant shift in the orientation of health care in the region. Amongst the factors mentioned in the statement were:

- '(The desire for) a new NHS in which population need and high quality services are the guiding principles.

- The resounding call from consumers for services to become more client centred and user friendly.
- The realisation that hospital care is not always the most effective method of provision for many services.
- Demands that resources be used more effectively and responsibly.
- (The pressure for) an explicit emphasis upon health promotion and disease prevention.'[23]

Clearly, every one of these factors can be said to point towards the emergence of a health care system based, to some extent, on the principles advocated here.

The willingness of many prestigious bodies to add their voices to those drawing attention to the limitations of the biomedical approach and the need for more far-reaching strategies, can also be regarded as a helpful development. For example, in 1991 the BMA accused the government of damaging public health by failing to provide adequate or sufficient housing and to act on research findings which suggested that there was a clear link between cigarette advertising and levels of smoking.[24]

Other bodies have gone further and are actively seeking to raise the profile of community based health care services, which they recognise as having a key role to play in developing a broader and more robust approach to health. In a report on community health (1992), the Audit Commission exhorted DHAs to end their neglect of CHSs, which they dubbed 'the Cinderella of the NHS.' The Commission pointed out that insufficient attention to community services in the past had led to the evolution of an illogical pattern of services. As a result of their findings, the Commission decided to undertake further more detailed reviews in relation to: needs based vision, strategic planning between districts, care coordination, management of service delivery, information systems and quality assurance.[25] Likewise, in its manifesto for community health nursing in the 1990s, the Royal College of Nursing asserted that community nurses should 'contribute to the determination of national and local health priorities' as well as the assessment of needs and the planning, commissioning and management of services in the community.[26] Also of significance is the House of Commons Select Committee on Health's report on maternity services (1992). In the view of the members of the committee, maternity care should be reshaped with effective midwifery support available in the community.[27] While the bodies concerned recognise the problems involved, the key point here is that there is a groundswell of informed opinion in favour of a broader approach to health and health care.

The consensus conferences sponsored by the King's Fund can also be regarded as a positive development in this respect. These have shown that it is possible to consider, 'in public, with a substantial lay element in the audience and a non-specialist majority on the panel', the effectiveness and efficiency of a wide variety of health care practices in both hospital and community settings (e.g. screening for breast cancer and for foetal and genetic abnormality; stroke treatment; blood cholesterol measurement in the prevention of coronary heart disease). In so doing, the participants have not only drawn upon the implicit knowledge of users and carers but also contributed towards its legitimisation. Similarly, by addressing ethical, as well as economic, aspects of alternative therapies and clinical interventions, they have demonstrated that values must be taken into account whenever health care decisions are being made and that priority should be given to the creation of mechanisms for this purpose.[28] It is perhaps significant that the need for this kind of development has been endorsed by bodies, such as the Nuffield Foundation, which has called for the establishment of a national ethics committee to counter the 'uncoordinated and often inadequate way in which problems in medical ethics are addressed.'[29] Moreover, it is very much in line with the decision of the WHO Regional Committee for Europe's decision to include a target specifically concerned with ethical issues (see Chapter 2).

At the same time, those involved with the education and training of health care personnel are reassessing what they teach with a view to accommodating some of the practices and values associated with a community oriented approach. For example, in the sphere of community nursing it has been recommended that service providers 'need specific knowledge, skills and attitudes in order to ... support informal carers in a partnership for the giving of care ...; search out and identify evolving health care needs ...; advise on the range of services ...; stimulate an awareness of health needs ...; empower people to take appropriate action to influence health policies ...; provide health data through health profiles ...; and undertake audit, review and appropriate quality assurance activities.'[30] It is also recognised that the education and training of community nurses should provide scope for multidisciplinary and interdisciplinary learning to enable them to work alongside those from other disciplines. 'Shared learning creates greater understanding of the contributions each discipline makes in caring for people in the community.'[31] Interestingly, this is taken a step further in the sphere of management education, where one of the benefits has been to bring together those from a variety of backgrounds. Not only are members of the managerial and clinical constituencies brought into contact with one another, but so also are those with a biomedical orientation and those who subscribe to the premises of a more social approach. In this way participants are obliged to take account of the different perspectives of their colleagues and may well begin to reassess their practice in the light of these insights.

In spite of the increasing demands being made on people's time and energy, the lay constituency is becoming more vocal and influential in its campaigning for changes to the health care system. It is gaining strength from the increasing interest of the consumer movement,[32] the green movement[33] and the feminist movement (see Chapter 3) in aspects of health care; the rapid growth in the number of informal carers; and the fact that men are becoming as keen as women to secure improvements in the quantity and quality of respite care. The continued willingness of the media, to date, to address consumer issues, particularly those within the field of health care, helps both to inform and to mobilise public opinion. Similarly various government initiatives, such as the Citizen's Charter and the Patient's Charter,[34] are fostering a climate within which the interests of service users and the principle of equality of access receive attention and acquire legitimacy.

Finally, one of the legacies of changes in higher education over the past three decades is that increasing numbers of women and members of ethnic minority communities are now ready and able to play key roles in the development of health care services from which they have traditionally been excluded. Many now possess the skills and competencies they need to contribute to the planning and delivery of services. Motivated by the desire to ensure that services reflect the needs and aspirations of those who in the past have been at the margins of health care, they are usually keen to respond positively to initiatives, such as Opportunity 2000,[35] based on the principle of equal opportunities, one of the hallmarks of a community oriented approach.

Despite the undoubted strengths of a community oriented approach to health care, it would clearly be wrong to suggest that it is a panacea. The nature of the 'crisis in health' is such that it will require action on a wide variety of fronts, such as housing, welfare benefits and transport, even to contain it. Nevertheless, it is contended that such an approach would go some way towards dealing with the 'crisis' and that many of the areas covered in this book are of far greater consequence for the health of the nation than the detailed administrative and organisational questions which have tended to preoccupy politicians, managers and service providers alike.

Although a community oriented approach is more likely to flourish where the administrative arrangements are such that the CHSs retain their separate identity, there are dangers in being too prescriptive on matters of this kind, especially at a time when the future shape of the health and social care system is so uncertain. In other words, it would be foolish and short-sighted to claim that the development of a community oriented approach is dependent upon the continued existence of community units and trusts. Of much greater significance is the level of commitment on the part of those who are in leadership positions within the health arena and their willingness and ability to challenge the dominance of the biomedically oriented hospital services which offer little in the way of a solution to the 'crisis in health'. Given that the distinction between commissioners and providers of health care is likely to be retained for the foreseeable future, particular attention must be paid to the content of service specifications. In so doing, commissioners will have a key role in ensuring that, as Ham has argued, priority is given 'to health promotion, public health and primary care services'.[36]

Unless there are significant moves in the direction of a community oriented approach, it will become increasingly difficult to meet the demands arising from epidemiological and demographic changes, especially given the pressure on resources. Moreover, public expectations will be thwarted and the possibility of securing greater equality with respect to access to health care will recede even further.

Notes

1 For a full discussion of the different types of power in social or organisational settings, see C. Handy, *Understanding Organisations* (London: Penguin Books, 1985), esp. pp.120-9.

2 Significantly, in 1992 the government introduced timed targets with respect to the percentage of women holding senior posts in the NHS. For example, by 1994 the percentage of women general managers should have increased from 18% to 30%; of consultants from 15.5% to 20%; and members of health authorities and trusts from 29% to 35%.

3 For a good example of this kind of study, see A. Oakley, 'Social support and pregnancy outcome', *British Journal of Obstetrics and Gynaecology*, no.97, 1990, pp.155-62. See also R. Smith, 'Research begins at forty', New Scientist, 30 June 1988, pp.54-8.

4 See A. Bowling, *Measuring Health: a review of quality of life measurement scales* (Milton Keynes: Open University Press, 1991).

5 This means expanding and emulating initiatives such as the North East Thames Region's Stimulating Nursing Research Fund. For details, see M. Lorentzon (ed.), *NETRHA Index of Nursing Research* (London: North East Thames Regional Health Authority, 1990).

6 See J. Seymour, 'Science on your doorstep: does damp housing make you ill?', *New Scientist*, 7 Dec 1991, pp.50-2.

7 C. Ham, *The New National Health Service: organisation and management* (Oxford: Radcliffe Medical Press Ltd, 1991), p.77.

8 For a discussion of the problems involved in securing a more collaborative approach to the provision of community based health care services, see R. Ottewill and A. Wall, *The Growth and Development of the Community Health Services* (Sunderland: Business Education Publishers, 1990), pp.500-3.

9 A. McNaught (ed.), *Managing Community Health Services* (London: Chapman and Hall, 1991), p.ix.

10 Under the contract, introduced in April 1990, GPs receive item of service payments for the vaccination and immunisation of children and cervical cytology screening if they reach certain targets; for child health surveillance work; and for holding health promotion clinics.

11 Under the practice staff scheme, FHSAs decide on the distribution between GPs of a cash limited sum for the reimbursement of all or part of the costs involved in employing non-medical support staff.

12 As a South Wales GP writing in *Medical World* in 1991 has commented, clinics of this kind 'are more of a gimmick than anything of substance ... and have created a new type of cynicism towards preventive work ... The new contract has produced a climate which makes (them) an economic

necessity for many practices. Consequently their main raison d'etre is finance generation rather than disease prevention.'

13 C. Hancock, for example, writing in the *THS Health Summary*, Nov 1990, has argued that, when set alongside cuts in community nursing services and in funded places for health visitor and district nurse training, the growth in the number of practice nurses has led community nurses 'to have understandable doubts about Department of Health and health authority commitment to the service.'

14 See, for example, J. Tudor-Hart et.al., 'Twenty five years of case finding and audit in a socially deprived community', *British Medical Journal*, vol.302, no.6791, 22 June 1991, pp.1509-13.

15 C. Hancock, op.cit.

16 It is important to make a distinction between 'managerialism' and 'management'. 'Managerialism' is an ideology founded on a belief in the virtues of economy and efficiency and the willingness to justify every action in these terms. 'Management' refers to the roles, responsibilities and activities of managers, who may or may not subscribe to the tenets of 'managerialism'. Indeed, because of their backgrounds, it is very unlikely that a majority of managers drawn from the clinical professions would adopt a 'managerialist' stance.

17 DH, *The Health of the Nation. A Consultative Document for Health in England*, Cmd 1523 (London: HMSO, 1991), Appendix 1, p.111.

18 See R. Ottewill and A. Wall, op.cit., pp.340-1 and pp.501-2.

19 See, for example, *Health Care Systems in Transition: the search for efficiency* (Paris: OECD, 1990) and D. Wilkin and C. Whitehouse, *General Practice in Five European Countries: Finland, Ireland, Netherlands, Spain, United Kingdom* (Geneva: WHO Regional Office for Europe, 1991). The definition of general practice which has been adopted in the WHO study stresses the importance of integrating physical, psychological and social factors in determining health status. In so doing, it goes beyond the biomedical emphasis within general practice which has traditionally prevailed in the UK. The impact on working practices of different methods of remunerating GPs and the importance of paying them a basic salary in order to secure a more socially oriented approach is also discussed.

20 Quoted by M. Dean, *The Lancet,* vol.338, 19 October 1991, p.1004.

21 Areas identified include: eating and drinking habits; accidents; health of pregnant women, infants and children; and mental health. For further details, see DH, op.cit., esp. ch.6.

22 Another example is the decision to set up 'a UK clearing house on outcomes ... responsible for collecting, collating, and disseminating information on health care outcomes assessment both from work done within the UK and abroad. It will also be available to provide expert advice

on resource requirements, methods, and data collection systems.' See NHS Management Executive, *Press Release*, H91/229, 16 May 1991.

23 Directorate of Nursing and Quality, *Nursing the Community: A consensus statement* (Bexhill on Sea: South East Thames Regional Health Authority, 1991), p.7.

24 Additionally, in 1992, the BMA in collaboration with other bodies, such as the Health Education Authority and Action on Smoking and Health, backed a poster advertising campaign designed to persuade MPs to support a ban on the advertising of tobacco products.

25 Audit Commission, *Homeward bound: a new course for community health* (London: HMSO, 1992).

26 The Royal College of Nursing, *Powerhouse for Change* (London: RCN, 1992).

27 House of Commons Paper No 29-I, Session 1991/2, Second Report from the Health Committee, *Maternity Services Volume 1 : Report together with Appendices and the Proceedings of the Committee* (London: HMSO, 1992).

28 For further information about these conferences, which are also referred to in Chapter 2, see B. Stocking, B. Jennett and J. Spiby, *Criteria for Change: the history and impact of consensus development conferences in the UK* (London: King's Fund Centre, 1991).

29 R. Nicholson, 'A National Ethics Committee Comes Closer', *THS Health Summary*, vol.viii, no.5, pp.12-3.

30 Community Education and Practice Group, *Report on Proposals for the Future of Community Education and Practice* (London: United Kingdom Central Council for Nursing, Midwifery and Health Visiting, 1991) pp.12-3.

31 Ibid., p.15.

32 For example, in 1991 a number of consumer groups urged the government to take various steps to reduce heart disease, such as banning cigarette advertising, raising taxes on tobacco and the introduction of better food labelling.

33 See, for example, P.Draper (ed), *Health Through Public Policy: The greening of public health* (London: Green Print, 1991) in which J. Porritt argues that 'from a Green perspective, there's no denying the idiocy of trying to keep a nation in good health when the majority of its citizens spend a fair part of their lives studiously undermining their own health!' (p.1).

34 The provisions of the Patient's Charter which are of particular relevance for a community oriented approach include the right to:

receive health care on the basis of clinical need, regardless of ability to pay;
clear explanations of treatment and alternatives; and
see personal medical records.

The 'national charter standards' include the requirement that:

a named qualified nurse, midwife or health visitor should be responsible for each patient;
hospitals should ensure that aftercare services are available for discharged patients; and
privacy and cultural beliefs must be respected.

35 This is a national campaign launched by John Major in 1991 and designed to boost women's involvement in the workforce. It is encouraging organisations to commit themselves publicly to improving the position of women by setting clear and unambiguous goals.

36 C. Ham, op.cit.

Index

D

N

O

P

Q

R